PLAIN ENGLISH

Book 4

Teacher's Annotated Edition

J. Martyn Walsh
Anna Kathleen Walsh

Random House/McCormick-Mathers

International Standard Book Number: 0-800-93018-5

Manufactured in the United States of America

To the Teacher

THE PLAIN ENGLISH HANDBOOK is the foundation upon which each book of the *Plain English* series is built. The *Handbook* treats so plainly the whole subject of English grammar and usage that students should not be without it. They are provided with easy-to-understand rules of grammar and usage, simple definitions, and clear examples. After they become familiar with its use, students will have in the *Plain English Handbook* a dependable guide to self-improvement in oral and written expression.

THE PLAIN ENGLISH SERIES provides a thorough mastery of the mechanics of English and effectively relates theory to usage, thus developing in the student a confidence in using the language. With the *Plain English* series, teachers can determine individual needs prior to the teaching of the units and then teach in accordance with these needs. They can supervise the learning activities of their students and give them help when needed. Thus much time is saved in mastering the fundamentals, and more time may be devoted to the improvement of oral and written expression. Each lesson in the *Plain English* series is keyed to pertinent sections of the *Plain English Handbook*.

PLAIN ENGLISH 4 is organized into five units. Each is preceded by a *Survey Test*, which gives a preview of the lessons contained in the unit. The *Survey Test* furthermore reveals to both student and teacher the areas where individual improvement is needed. So that students may be made aware of their own special weaknesses, it is suggested that they be permitted to grade their own *Survey Tests* and note their scores on the *Score Chart* on the inside back cover of the book. Many teachers have the students score their own lessons as well because they have found that the students benefit noticeably from the corrective self-evaluation gained through this experience. To measure individual progress, an *Inventory* of each unit has been provided at the end of the book. This *Inventory* parallels, in content, the *Survey Test*. A *Final Inventory* in four forms, A, B, C, and D, measures individual progress for the complete course.

The Activities which follow many of the lessons provide enrichment for those students who are well grounded in English fundamentals, corrective opportunity for those students who need it, and an opportunity for all students to apply recently acquired knowledge of correct usage.

Spelling Lists are effectively spaced throughout *Plain English 4*. Each of the ten lists contains forty words that are frequently used and frequently misspelled.

Vocabulary Studies are also found at the end of the book. These twenty-two studies are parallel in construction to many standardized vocabulary tests. Taken at intervals throughout the year, the vocabulary studies help students to add to their vocabulary and check up on their own vocabulary growth.

Plain English 4 provides English students with a comprehensive study guide and with adequate practice opportunity to insure maximum mastery and retention.

Contents

Sentence Completeness

This test parallels, in content, Inventory 1, page 103.

I. *Sentence Sense*

   (Lessons 1, 2)   15 Points

On the line preceding each group of words, write **o** if the group is not a complete sentence; write **1** if the group is one complete sentence; or write **2** if the group is two sentences incorrectly written as one.

EXAMPLE: _2_ I am going to meet Alicia would you like to go with me?

_2_ 1 Pat has good ideas she will surely be a good president.

_0_ 2 Saw Bud and Sue at the show's last performance last night.

_1_ 3 Ask for a receipt when you pay your dues.

_0_ 4 While Betty and Danny were shopping.

_1_ 5 It is a perfect day for the game and everyone is excited.

_2_ 6 Kay is not here now she is the new chairperson of the committee.

_1_ 7 Phil and Juan sold all their tickets and collected the money for them.

_0_ 8 When the day finally arrived for their boat trip.

_2_ 9 Studying music is interesting have you ever played the piano?

_0_ 10 Skiing down the steep mountains in a blinding snowstorm.

_2_ 11 It was a very funny comedy you shouldn't have missed it.

_1_ 12 We cleaned up the living room after the other guests had gone home.

_2_ 13 Marge was here this afternoon I am sorry you couldn't come.

_0_ 14 Snow-capped peaks gleaming in the summer sunlight.

_1_ 15 Driving through the mountains, we saw a herd of buffalo.

5

II. *Essential Parts of a Sentence*

   (Lesson 3)   20 Points

Draw one line under the simple subject and draw two lines under the simple predicate of each sentence.

EXAMPLE: Did Jan go to Maine last summer?

1 Did the Sioux Indians live in New England at any time?

2 Around the corner came a large, fast, white camper.

3 Laughing noisily at their games, the children did not hear us.

4 Did you see Starr Walton, the famous skier, at the last party?

5 Just beyond that hill is a small lake used as a bird sanctuary.

6 After the cold and gloom of winter comes spring.

7 Has Julie been writing the history of her family?

8 Have you seen any of Shakespeare's plays presented on television?

9 Hoping for a scholarship, Robin has been working at home constantly.

10 Have the plans for your committee meeting been completed?

III. *Combining Groups of Words*

(Lessons 5–10)   65 Points

Make one complete sentence of the two groups of words in each item by changing punctuation and capitalization. On the line preceding the sentence you reconstruct, give its class by writing **S** for simple, **Cd** for compound, or **Cx** for complex. Above each italicized word, give its part of speech. Use abbreviations.

EXAMPLE: Cx Jim and I *cleaned* the garage/ ~~After~~ you went home.
                        v   *after*

Cd 1 Stan Blake is the *captain* of the team. /He is a quarterback.
                        n   *h*

Cx 2 Although she was *greatly* handicapped, /She has become a famous athlete.
                        adv   *s*

S 3 Zooming across the *cloudless* sky, /The jets made a startling noise.
                        adj   *t*

Cx 4 You *surely* will have to work hard. /If *you* expect to finish your costume by tonight.
              adv   *i pron*

Cd 5 Eugene is intensely interested *in* music; /He would like to become a pianist.
                                    prep   *h*

Cd 6 Ann is an extremely fast runner; /Consequently, she *is* a *valuable* sprinter.
                                        c   *v v* *adj*

Cd 7 Tracy's stories are *always* interesting; /Someday he may be a *fine* novelist.
                          adv   *s*   *adj*

Cd 8 Lucy will not win the prize; /She is *careless* with all her work.
                                  s   *adj*

Cd 9 William Saroyan *wrote* "The Parsley Garden"; /It is a story about a teen-aged boy.
                      v   *i*

Cd 10 Helen delivers papers every morning; /Yet not once has *she* made poor grades.
                                           v   *pron*

Cd 11 Nell *and* I mowed the lawn. /Our other neighbors and Bill played stickball.
            conj   *o*

Cx 12 If you cannot get a *plane* reservation, /You may have to go by train or bus.
                          adj   *v*

Cd 13 *Jan* went to a dance last night; /It *was* the first time she had been to one.
       n   *i* *v*

Cx 14 If you don't know Lee's telephone number, /You *will find* it in the directory.
                                               v   *v v*

Cd 15 Helen Grayson is *unusually* clever. /However, she is very careless in her *speech*.
                       adv   *h*   *n*

S 16 Fred worked day after day, /Hoping to win *the* scholarship.
                               h   *adj*

S 17 Georgia likes all kinds of stories. /Especially stories of *adventure*.
                                         e   *n*

Cx 18 If *you* hope to win the tournament, /You are going to have to practice more.
          pron   *v*

Cx 19 When you see your *sister*, /Please give her this message.
                        n   *p*

Cx 20 After the game ended in defeat *for* us, /We dropped our plans for a celebration.
                                     prep   *w*

SCORE _____ (Top Score 100)

LESSON 1

Sentence Sense/1

On the line preceding each group of words, write **0** if the group is not a complete sentence; write **1** if the group is one complete sentence; or write **2** if the group is two sentences incorrectly written as one.

EXAMPLE: _2_ Old Silas loved the gold dearly he had nothing else in the world to love.

_0_ 1 Regarding the child as his own.

_1_ 2 The old man wished Eppie to be happy.

_1_ 3 He had been unjustly accused of stealing.

_1_ 4 He felt that Eppie was a gift from heaven.

_0_ 5 Telling Silas that she would like a garden.

_1_ 6 The lonely old man wished to keep the child.

_0_ 7 Silas Marner in disgrace leaving Lantern Yard.

_1_ 8 Put yourself in the lonely old weaver's place.

_0_ 9 Nancy always insisting that Eppie do her duty.

_1_ 10 Try to realize just what the loss meant to Silas.

_1_ 11 Soon Eppie changed the life of the lonely old man.

_2_ 12 Aaron Winthrop was much like his mother he liked to help others.

_0_ 13 Eppie growing up to be a favorite in the small community.

_1_ 14 Dolly Winthrop and Aaron also called to see Silas.

_2_ 15 The money had meant everything to him it was all that he had.

_0_ 16 Godfrey Cass, fearing to admit that the child was his.

_2_ 17 The old man soon ceased to love gold he was no longer a miser.

_2_ 18 Godfrey Cass was indeed a selfish creature he deserved to be childless.

_0_ 19 Always eager to do something to make other people happy.

_1_ 20 The old man regained much of the faith that he had lost.

_0_ 21 Going immediately to the Rainbow and accusing Jem Rodney.

_2_ 22 We admire her for refusing to go with Godfrey she really belonged to Silas.

_0_ 23 Godfrey and Nancy selfishly hoping to win Eppie away from Silas.

_2_ 24 She looked upon Silas as her father no one else could take his place.

_2_ 25 Eppie was considerate of her father she surely was a good daughter.

Plain English Handbook, 1–4, 34–37.

Activity: The beginning of the school year is a very good time to practice making introductions. This is a good opportunity to become acquainted with the classmates you do not yet know. Practice introducing your teacher to your classmates and introducing classmates to one another. *Plain English Handbook,* 642 (16).

SCORE _____ (Top Score 25)

7

Sentence Sense/2

On the line preceding each group of words, write **o** if the group is not a complete sentence; write **1** if the group is one complete sentence; write **2** if the group is two sentences incorrectly written as one; or write **3** if the group is three sentences incorrectly written as one.

EXAMPLE: _2_ Flags flutter from the stadium a runner carries a torch into the arena.

_1_ 1 Every four years, amateur athletes from many nations compete in the Olympic Games.

_0_ 2 The purpose of the Olympic Games to let the great amateur athletes compete.

_2_ 3 The Summer Olympics run for about two weeks the Winter Olympics last ten days.

_0_ 4 Relying on individual citizens to pay their Olympic expenses.

_1_ 5 No other sport spectacle has a background so historic, dramatic, or thrilling.

_2_ 6 Behind their flags the athletes march into the stadium they stand at attention.

_1_ 7 A runner carries a blazing torch to announce the opening of the Olympic Games.

_3_ 8 The trumpets play pigeons are released from their cages the Olympic Games are open.

_2_ 9 The Summer Games include track events each sport must be carried by 20 countries.

_0_10 In the bob-sledding events, two- or four-member teams.

_2_11 Nations do not actually compete against each other no nation officially wins.

_3_12 Skiing is a Winter Game figure skating is a popular event there are races, also.

_0_13 In the ancient Olympics, sacrifices of grain, wine, and lambs.

_1_14 The early games included competition in art forms as well as in athletics.

_0_15 Criers announcing the winners' names throughout the land.

_1_16 Women were excluded from the ancient Games as competitors and spectators.

_0_17 If practiced in accordance with the ancient Greek ideals.

_2_18 The exact date of the first games is unknown the first recorded race was in 776 B.C.

_3_19 The first races were in Elis, Greece the races honored Zeus Zeus was a Greek god.

_2_20 The ancient games were abolished in 392 A.D. the modern games were begun in 1896.

8

Plain English Handbook, 1–4, 34–37.

Activity: On a separate sheet of paper, make complete sentences of the incomplete sentences above. You will find information about the Olympic Games in your encyclopedia.

SCORE_____(Top Score 20)

Essential Parts of the Sentence

Draw one line under the simple subject and draw two lines under the simple predicate of each sentence.

EXAMPLE: Amelia Earhart flew across the Atlantic Ocean by herself in 1932.

1 The airplane is the most amazing invention of the modern world.

2 People have been thinking of flying for hundreds of years.

3 Leonardo da Vinci drew the earliest known design for a helicopter about 1500.

4 Sir George Cayley frequently is called "the father of the airplane."

5 Otto Lilienthal's gliding research in 1895 led to the invention of the airplane.

6 The first successful fliers were the Wright brothers.

7 Orville Wright's first flight was just 120 feet.

8 Today there are jets that can make nonstop flights of 12,500 miles without refueling.

9 The first planes were largely built of canvas, bamboo, and steel wire.

10 During the early 1900's, daring pilots broke aviation records almost every week.

11 Baroness Raymonde de Laroche of France became the first licensed woman pilot in 1910.

12 The first airplane race in the United States was held in 1910.

13 The first round-the-world flight, in 1924, took 175 days.

14 Charles Lindbergh made the first nonstop transatlantic solo flight in 1927.

15 In 1957 three jet bombers flew around the world in 45 hours.

16 Aviation has created new growth patterns for many cities of the world.

17 In some areas of the world rice is now sown from airplanes.

18 Airplanes are also used for crop dusting as well as for air freight.

19 Many private persons now pilot their own airplanes.

20 A well-known poem about flying is "Darius Green and His Flying Machine."

Plain English Handbook, 3, 4, 13, 15.

Activity: On the lines at the bottom of the page, write a paragraph of at least five sentences. Draw one line under each simple subject and draw two lines under each simple predicate.

_____

_____

_____

_____

_____

SCORE _____ (Top Score 40)

LESSON 4

Predicate Nominative or Appositive

Draw one line under each appositive and draw two lines under each predicate nominative.

EXAMPLE: Casca, the first <u>man</u> to strike Caesar, was a decided <u>radical</u>.

1 Calpurnia was Caesar's <u>wife</u>.

2 Brutus surely was not a great <u>leader</u>.

3 This story of Roman life, as told in *Julius Caesar*, is a grim <u>tragedy</u>.

4 Portia, the <u>wife</u> of Brutus, was Cato's <u>daughter</u>.

5 Titinius, a good <u>friend</u> of Cassius, killed himself.

6 Do you think that Marc Antony, Caesar's <u>grand-nephew</u>, was an effective <u>speaker</u>?

7 Cassius, the leading <u>conspirator</u>, envied all great men.

8 Cassius and Brutus were poor <u>commanders</u> of an army.

9 An interesting character is <u>Lucius</u>, the sleepy <u>musician</u>.

10 Flavius, the <u>tribune</u>, was not a <u>friend</u> of Julius Caesar.

11 Ligarius, the "sick" <u>man</u>, became an ardent <u>conspirator</u>.

12 Cinna, the wily <u>conspirator</u>, was not <u>Cinna</u>, the able <u>poet</u>.

13 The author of this play is <u>William Shakespeare</u>, the great Elizabethan <u>dramatist</u>.

14 Brutus, a great <u>lover</u> of books, placed honor above all else.

15 Perhaps the greatest weakness of Brutus was poor <u>judgment</u>.

16 Brutus, Caesar's best <u>friend</u>, was startled by Caesar's ghost.

17 Artemidorus, the wise <u>teacher</u>, wrote a warning note to Caesar.

18 Did Antony think that the conspirators were honorable <u>men</u>?

19 Brutus, the impractical <u>idealist</u>, sacrificed Caesar, his good <u>friend</u>.

20 In this play Brutus, the desperate <u>conspirator,</u> was a faithless <u>friend</u>.

Plain English Handbook, 96, 100, 101.

Activity: On the lines below, write a short paragraph in which you use predicate nominatives and words in apposition. Mark them as you did in the lesson above.

_____

_____

_____

_____

_____

10

LESSON 5

Capitalization and Punctuation

Insert punctuation marks where they are needed. Cross out each incorrect mark and each incorrectly capitalized word and write the correct form above it. The numbers in parentheses refer to the *Plain English Handbook*.

history

EXAMPLE: Hal Sloan, Pat's cousin, is studying ~~History~~ this summer.   (500, 471)

1 Edouard Manet a F̲french artist, painted "The B̲boy with a S̲sword."   (500, 468, 478)

2 Fighting ceased in World W̲war I on N̲november 11, 1918.   (473, 469, 502)

3 Bill saw C̲ćapt. George H. Hall last S̲summer.   (481, 487, 470)

4 When our principal said, D̲"do your best for Webb H̲high School," we responded whole-heartedly.   (487, 466, 471, 501, 507)

5 Michiko likes Christina G. Rossetti's poem "Goblin M̲market."   (487, 500, 478)

6 On Tuesday, May 10, Jackie will be twenty-one years old.   (502, 534)

7 Julio Martinez is from the S̲śouth; however he is going to school in the N̲ńorth.   (474, 490)

8 Margaret Freeman, a C̲ćanadian girl in our class, is studying m̲Mathematics.   (500, 468, 471)

9 A line of Lewis Carroll's poem is "B̲ƀeware the J̲jabberwock, my son!"   (519, 465, 468)

10 Abraham Lincoln read the following books when he was a child: the B̲ƀible, *Robinson Crusoe*, and *The Pilgrim's Progress*.   (493, 477, 504)

11 My brother is studying S̲śpanish this W̲Winter; therefore he keeps very busy.   (471, 470, 490)

12 Is the P̲president a member of the R̲republican P̲party.?   (482, 471, 529)

13 When Father and I were in the city, we saw M̲major Green and her S̲śister, Sharon.   (497, 481, 482)

14 Carl Sandburg, who wrote "Chicago" and other poems, is an A̲ámerican poet.   (499, 468)

15 T̲ŧall, slender, graceful pines stand at the entrance to our h̲High S̲School.   (464, 505, 471)

16 Jack and I̲í saw G̲ģeneral Clay in Dallas, Texas, last W̲Winter.   (479, 481, 500, 470)

17 Mr. John A̲á. Meyner asked us if we were j̲Juniors in Hale C̲ćollege.?   (480, 471, 486, 529)

18 There are twenty-three students who study French and S̲śpanish.   (534, 471)

19 Margaret went to Mills College, we are told, to study E̲énglish and L̲ĺatin.   (500, 471)

20 Yes, I wrote my essay on W̲world W̲war II; however my teacher hasn't read it yet.   (498, 473, 490)

SCORE _____ (Top Score 75)

Combining Sentences

On the line provided, combine the two simple sentences in each item to form one simple sentence. You may do this by making either the subject or the predicate compound or by using an appositive. Be sure that your punctuation is correct.   (Correct answers may vary.)

EXAMPLE: Fred is our football captain. He is a leader in all sports.
Fred, a leader in all sports, is our football captain.

1 Kay went to a picnic. Jan went to the picnic, too.
Kay and Jan went to the picnic.

2 Mrs. Wilson is our new principal. She seems to be an excellent speaker.
Mrs. Wilson, our new principal, seems to be an excellent speaker.

3 Marjorie Kinnan Rawlings wrote *The Yearling*. It is a story about life in Florida.
Marjorie Kinnan Rawlings wrote *The Yearling,* a story about life in Florida.

4 James Thurber has written many books. He has illustrated them himself.
James Thurber has written and illustrated many books.

5 Naomi worked on a ranch last summer. Carlos worked on the same ranch.
Naomi and Carlos worked on the same ranch last summer.

6 Mary and Bill are in our class. They are both excellent musicians.
Mary and Bill, excellent musicians, are in our class.

7 Juan Gomez is a sensitive, compassionate poet. He is also a good harmonica player.
Juan Gomez, a sensitive, compassionate poet, is also a good harmonica player.

8 The boys and girls played games. They also sang folk songs.
The boys and girls played games and sang folk songs.

9 Jo Grant is a member of our club. She is an outstanding leader.
Jo Grant, an outstanding leader, is a member of our club.

10 Frank Shaw lives in Boston. Tom Stone lives there, too.
Frank Shaw and Tom Stone live in Boston.

11 Juanita won the scholarship. She is the youngest person in our class.
Juanita, the youngest person in our class, won a scholarship.

12 The officers of our class wrote the invitations. Then they mailed them.
The officers of our class wrote and mailed the invitations.

13 Beth wants to be an atomic scientist. She is our class president.
Beth, our class president, wants to be an atomic scientist.

14 Janie Day went to Canada. Mac Williams went with her.
Janie Day and Mac Williams went to Canada.

15 Tom Smith bought a new car. He is my brother's closest friend.
Tom Smith, my brother's closest friend, bought a new car.

Plain English Handbook, 17, 18, 101, 500.

SCORE _____ (Top Score 15)

Completing Complex Sentences

There are two simple sentences in each item below. On the line provided, rewrite these two sentences to form one **complex** sentence. Be sure that your punctuation is correct. (Correct answers may vary.)

EXAMPLE: Jan and Terry swam. John and Dana played golf.
While Jan and Terry swam, John and Dana played golf.

1 Sue studied art many years. She had an exhibit of her work in 1974.
Sue, who studied art many years, had an exhibit of her work in 1974.

2 Bob is critical. He rarely offers suggestions.
Although Bob is critical, he rarely offers suggestions.

3 Newborn ants are small. They have been poorly nourished.
Newborn ants are small because they have been poorly nourished.

4 Enrico was late to school. He missed his usual bus.
Enrico was late to school because he missed his usual bus.

5 Pat began her novel last summer. She was on vacation.
Pat began her novel last summer when she was on vacation.

6 Marcia studies hard. She hopes to win a scholarship.
Marcia, who hopes to win a scholarship, studies hard.

7 Our football team should do well. They worked very hard in practice.
Since our football team worked very hard in practice, they should do well.

8 Bill completed the entire outline. Helen wrote the story.
Bill completed the entire outline before Helen wrote the story.

9 I was very hungry. I fixed an enormous club sandwich.
Since I was very hungry, I fixed an enormous club sandwich.

10 Hal raced across the goal line. The crowd went wild with joy.
As Hal raced across the goal line, the crowd went wild with joy.

11 The other girls went to a show. Ruth and I played checkers.
While the other girls went to a show, Ruth and I played checkers.

12 Red is his favorite color. I am making him a red plaid shirt.
Since red is his favorite color, I am making him a red plaid shirt.

13 Tom did not accept Milton's invitation. He had other plans.
Tom, who had other plans, did not accept Milton's invitation.

14 Jane is a perfectionist. Her work is always done well.
Jane, whose work is always done well, is a perfectionist.

15 Gail Gault has a keen sense of humor. She can be serious, too.
Gail Gault, who has a keen sense of humor, can be serious, too.

Plain English Handbook, 23, 414, 497.

13

SCORE _____ (Top Score 15)

Combining Sentences

There are two simple sentences in each item below. On a separate sheet of paper, combine these two sentences in four ways: (1) as a simple sentence, (2) as a compound sentence with the clauses connected by a conjunction, (3) as a compound sentence with the clauses connected by punctuation, and (4) as a complex sentence. Be sure that your punctuation and capitalization are correct. (Review Lessons 6 and 7.)
(Correct answers may vary.)

EXAMPLE: Henry Burr worked on a farm last summer. He learned much about country life.

(1) Working on a farm last summer, Henry Burr learned much about country life. (2) Henry Burr worked on a farm last summer, and he learned much about country life. (3) Henry Burr worked on a farm last summer; he learned much about country life. (4) While he worked on a farm last summer, Henry Burr learned much about country life.

1 I traveled through New England last summer. I was particularly impressed with Cape Cod.
2 George Bernard Shaw wrote many delightful plays. He is popular with many people.
3 That young artist struggled a long time in poverty. She is now successful.
4 Hal Mason is unusually clever. He will do well at the university.
5 Terry Reeves is very much interested in design. He hopes to be a fashion designer.
6 The climate in those mountains is pleasant in summer. In winter it is extremely cold.
7 Ed found an advertisement for a lifeguard. He hurried to apply for the job.
8 Most of us shun the difficult task. Only through hard work can we achieve great things.
9 Sandra has a smile for everyone. Never does she seem unhappy.
10 Our team is working hard in football. They hope to win the game on Saturday.
11 Tom and I finished all our work in the morning. In the afternoon we played tennis.
12 Jack Bailey is extremely conceited. He is not popular with the other students.
13 The professor is very scholarly. He recently published another book.
14 Lou writes excellent stories. Sometimes she uses dialect to add to the effect.
15 Lila is greatly interested in the study of law. Someday she may be a famous attorney.

Plain English Handbook, 20–23, 390, 410, 414, 415, 455, 490, 497.

Activity: Write a letter to a department store, ordering at least five pieces of merchandise. Read sections 587–603 of *Plain English Handbook* for the requirements and correct form of a business letter. Section 603 makes specific suggestions concerning a letter ordering merchandise.

Spelling List/1

advise	disagreeable	irrigate	visible	possible
assistance	scissors	territory	syllable	reasonably
relieve	unique	ordinarily	responsible	ability
impatient	people	instance	remarkable	difficulty
shrieks	especially	attendance	desirable	hastily
knowledge	valleys	wholly	positive	necessity
behavior	revealed	allowed	capable	mechanical
anxious	debtor	already	advisable	notified

SCORE _____ (Top Score 60)

Completing Sentences

By changing capitalization and punctuation, make a complete sentence — simple, compound, or complex — of each of the following items.

EXAMPLES:
Bob saw many well-known people/ ~~While~~ *while* he was in New York.

Expecting to attend the hockey game/ ~~We~~ *, we* had an early dinner.

1 Janet had many exciting times/ ~~While~~ *while* she lived in Chicago.

2 Longing to become a great scientist/ ~~That~~ *that* young man is working very hard.

3 Jean and I were pleased with the plans the other members offered objections.

4 Hal likes adventure stories/ ~~Particularly~~ *particularly* stories of the old West.

5 Ann saw many famous actors/ ~~When~~ *when* she was in Hollywood last summer.

6 Planning to start on our trip early the next morning/ ~~We~~ *we* went to bed early.

7 Beth and I had most of the work done/ ~~Before~~ *before* the other people arrived.

8 Fred surely can't expect to win/ ~~Unless~~ *unless* he improves his tennis game.

9 Steve and Manuela have arranged the tables. Al and Kim will serve refreshments.

10 Kay Strong has appeared on many television shows/ ~~Since~~ *since* she went to New York.

11 Edgar Allan Poe wrote horror stories in prose; his poetry was usually sad.

12 Bill is studying the contrabassoon; it is a woodwind instrument with a very low sound.

13 The other couples waited at the dock/ ~~Until~~ *until* Nancy and I arrived.

14 After the basketball game was ended/ ~~We~~ *we* planned a big celebration.

15 Ted struggled year after year/ ~~Hoping~~ *hoping* to become a great writer.

16 When Jill went to college. ~~She~~ *she* decided to major in journalism.

17 Overcoming many obstacles/ Booker T. Washington became a leader in education.

18 If you expect to go to Europe in two years/ ~~You~~ *you* will have to be more thrifty now.

19 Paul Laurence Dunbar wrote many lyrics, he wrote both serious and humorous poems.

20 Since he wrote about black life honestly/ ~~His~~ *his* works are important historically.

Plain English Handbook, 20–23, 33–37, 490, 495, 497, 499.

Activity: Select a book from the library and prepare an oral book report to give before the class. *Plain English Handbook*, 645.

15

SCORE _____ (Top Score 20)

LESSON 10

Classifying Sentences and Parts of Speech

On the line preceding each sentence, indicate its class by writing **S** for simple, **Cd** for compound, or **Cx** for complex. Above each italicized word, indicate its part of speech by writing **n** for noun, **pron** for pronoun, **adj** for adjective, **adv** for adverb, **v** for verb, **prep** for preposition, or **conj** for conjunction. Class the conjunctive adverb (320) and pronoun (135) as conjunctions.

EXAMPLE: __Cx__ Tom doesn't know *where he* lost his canteen. *(n above Tom; conj above where; pron above he)*

S ___ 1 We six *girls* started on our camping *trip early* Saturday morning. *(n, n, adv)*

Cd ___ 2 We *packed* our gear carefully, *but* we still had too much to carry *comfortably*. *(v, conj, adv)*

Cd ___ 3 There *were* only six girls on the trip, *yet* it seemed liked a *larger* group. *(v, conj, adj)*

Cx ___ 4 We hiked *through* the *woods while* the others finished unpacking their equipment. *(prep, n, conj)*

S ___ 5 The *park* guide wouldn't allow *us* to walk *over* the old, rotted bridge. *(adj, pron, prep)*

Cx ___ 6 If we *hike* steadily, we can *reach* the next campsite *before* dark. *(v, v, prep)*

Cx ___ 7 *This* fire has consumed all *those* logs *that* we brought from the woods. *(adj, adj, conj)*

S ___ 8 Jan *and* the *other* girls have gone to look for some good *firewood*. *(conj, adj, n)*

Cx ___ 9 We put up the tents *very* quickly *after* we had built a *roaring* fire. *(adv, conj, adj)*

Cx ___ 10 There were *four* girls *who* took charge of the cooking *chores*. *(adj, conj, n)*

S ___ 11 *We* had good weather all the *time except* Friday evening. *(pron, n, prep)*

S ___ 12 There are *only* three girls swimming *in* the lake *now*. *(adv, prep, adv)*

Cx ___ 13 *Show* me the *stream* that the *others* have found. *(v, n, pron)*

S ___ 14 *Linda* and I *caught* fifteen *fish* today. *(n, v, n)*

S ___ 15 We *watched* the *curious* bear cub carefully knock over our garbage *pail*. *(v, adj, n)*

Cd ___ 16 The mother bear *looked* harmless, *but* we did *not* get close enough to find out! *(v, conj, adv)*

Cx ___ 17 *This* is the sleeping bag *that* Jean borrowed *from* her parents, who camp often. *(pron, conj, prep)*

Cx ___ 18 Ms. Allen, our leader, *was* very pleased *when* we *identified* some constellations. *(v, conj, v)*

Cx ___ 19 We must be sure to put out *this fire before* we leave the park. *(adj, n, conj)*

Cd ___ 20 Our camping *trip* was a great success, *and* it was very *instructive*. *(n, conj, adj)*

Plain English Handbook, 20–23, 38–45, 52, 138–140.

Activity: Write a short paragraph that contains ten simple sentences. Rewrite your paragraph combining the simple sentences to form five compound or complex sentences.

SCORE _____ (Top Score 80)

16

Verbs

This test parallels, in content, Inventory 2, page 105.

I. *Transitive and Intransitive Verbs*

(Lessons 11, 12)   10 Points

Draw one line under each transitive verb and two lines under each intransitive verb. Be sure to underline the entire verb.

EXAMPLE: <u>Has</u> your brother <u>sent</u> the book to you?

1 Why <u>did</u> Sue <u>send</u> the picture to me?

2 <u>Has</u> he <u>invited</u> all the seniors to his party?

3 The ocean <u>looked</u> gray and shimmering in the moon's light.

4 The sophomores <u>have been playing</u> some rough games.

5 He <u>should have helped</u> Dan with the report.

6 The sun <u>shines</u> brightly this morning.

7 Mercedes <u>has been writing</u> letters to her family in Mexico.

8 Did Mike <u>speak</u> well before the meeting yesterday?

9 <u>Has</u> the report <u>been sent</u> to the secretary?

10 They <u>should have been planning</u> the program for next week.

II. *Tenses of Verbs*

(Lessons 12–18)   15 Points

In each sentence write the correct tense form of the verb in parentheses.

EXAMPLE: (sing — present perfect)   Lee _____*has sung*_____ her solo already.

1 (**swim** — past perfect)   Kay _____had swum_____ across the river yesterday.

2 (**rise** — past perfect)   The moon _____had risen_____ before we started to leave.

3 (**do** — present perfect)   Dick _____has done_____ his part unusually well tonight.

4 (**lay** — past)   The dog _____laid_____ himself down on the old rug.

5 (**sit** — present perfect)   They _____have sat_____ there ever since the bell rang.

6 (**know** — past)   Jean _____knew_____ that we would do our part.

7 (**lie** — past perfect)   The kitten _____ had lain _____ there a long while before we left.

8 (**see** — past)   Jim _____ saw _____ Clair at the dance last night.

9 (**take** — past perfect)   She _____ had taken _____ the book before you came.

10 (**run** — past)   Jack and I _____ ran _____ to the pool and jumped in.

11 (**lie** — past)   The dog _____ lay _____ in the shade while we were working.

12 (**go** — past perfect)   Gene _____ had gone _____ before we arrived at the station.

13 (**give** — past)   Tom _____ gave _____ Lisa some old coins for her collection.

14 (**eat** — present perfect)   The little dog _____ has eaten _____ the large piece of meat.

15 (**come** — past)   Louise _____ came _____ to school with Nan and me.

III. *Using Verbs*

(Lessons 19–26)   25 Points

Cross out each incorrect verb and write the correct form above it.

sat

EXAMPLE: Joe and she came in and ~~set~~ at a table near the door.

come
1 Here ~~comes~~ Mr. Hall and his students.
        spoken   rose
2 The man had not ~~spoke~~ until he ~~raised~~ to his feet.
      were   did
3 The class thinks you ~~was~~ the one who ~~done~~ the best work this year.
                am
4 Are you sure it is I who ~~is~~ to make this report?
   were   done
5 If I ~~was~~ he, I'd do as the others have ~~did~~.
                  are
6 Hank is one of those people who ~~is~~ always eager for fun.
                    were   came
7 Neither Miss Field nor the speakers ~~was~~ here when we ~~come~~.
 Were   saw
8 ~~Was~~ Bob and his sister at the airport when you ~~seen~~ them?
   doesn't   gone
9 Fred ~~don't~~ know whether the other boys have ~~went~~ home or not.
            lying   came
10 The puppy has been ~~laying~~ beside the heater since he ~~come~~ in.
                    is
11 We don't know which one of the girls ~~are~~ selling the tickets.
      was   gave
12 Our glee club ~~were~~ invited to sing when they ~~give~~ their last party.
          were   ran
13 A great number of students ~~was~~ here when Dick ~~run~~ in the contest.
      began   given
14 Before the rain ~~begun~~ to fall, we had done the work she had ~~gave~~ us.
                              was
15 After the hard work we had done, bread and butter ~~were~~ good food.

SCORE _____ (Top Score 50)

Classes of Verbs

Draw one line under each transitive verb and draw two lines under each intransitive verb. Be sure to underline all parts of the verb.

EXAMPLE: Have all the sophomores <u>bought</u> tickets for the seniors' variety show?

1 Tina surely <u>did</u> well in the contest last night.
2 <u>Did</u> your team <u>defeat</u> ours in the soccer game yesterday?
3 <u>Has</u> the new committee <u>arranged</u> the next program?
4 Jack <u>sang</u> two songs for us at the party last night.
5 When <u>did</u> Alice <u>return</u> from her trip to New Orleans?
6 That cat <u>has been sitting</u> on the fence for an hour or more.
7 The other girls <u>must have brought</u> the props for the stage.
8 Helena <u>is writing</u> interesting stories about her recent trip to Spain.
9 <u>Did</u> Liza and Henry <u>play</u> tennis this morning before school?
10 <u>Shall</u> we <u>play</u> another game of badminton now, or after lunch?

Plain English Handbook, 173–176, 212.

Draw one line under each complete verb and draw two lines under each linking (copulative) verb.

EXAMPLE: We <u>sat</u> beside the old mill for about an hour.

11 There <u>are</u> many excellent students in our school this year.
12 The little girl <u>ran</u> happily around the newly mown field.
13 Many children <u>played</u> among the big trees in the park.
14 We <u>camped</u> for a month in the Green Mountains of Vermont.
15 The old cabin <u>stood</u> on a little hill above the foot trail.
16 In the autumn evening we <u>sat</u> around a cheerful campfire.
17 The Appalachian Mountains in North Carolina <u>look</u> beautiful in their autumn colors.
18 Our principal <u>has gone</u> to a meeting of educators in the East.
19 That <u>is</u> certainly the most unusual car in the automobile show this year.
20 We <u>looked</u> across the great plains toward the high mountains.

Plain English Handbook, 177, 178, 180.

Activity: Write sentences using each of the following verbs, or a form of each of the verbs, as a transitive verb and as an intransitive verb. Then classify each verb as regular or irregular. *Plain English Handbook,* 171, 172, 176.

1 sing	3 drive	5 study	7 turn
2 move	4 help	6 eat	8 meet

SCORE _____ (Top Score 20)

19

Classes and Modifications of Verbs

Indicate the class of each italicized verb by writing **t** above it if it is transitive or **i** if it is intransitive. If the verb is transitive, indicate its voice by writing **a** for active or **p** for passive after the **t**. If the verb is intransitive, indicate whether it is complete or linking by writing **c** or **l** after the **i**.

EXAMPLE: Jack Barry *is* the best swimmer at our local YMCA.
(i-l)

1 I *should have been preparing* my Spanish lesson for tomorrow. *(t-a)*

2 That lazy student *might have been* the leader of our class. *(i-l)*

3 The horses cantering along the bridle path *were* tired. *(i-l)*

4 More than half of the students in our school band *are* juniors. *(i-l)*

5 This delightful book *was written* by a little-known American author. *(t-p)*

6 We *had* a good time at the picnic in the park yesterday. *(t-a)*

7 Our basketball team *has been defeated* only once this season. *(t-p)*

8 We *fished* in a little mountain stream near a pine forest. *(i-c)*

9 East High's best player *became* angry during the game yesterday. *(i-l)*

10 The seniors *are working* on their assembly program for next week. *(i-c)*

Plain English Handbook, 173–180, 184, 185, 212.

Indicate the tense of each verb by writing above it **pres** for present, **past** for past, **fut** for future, **pres per** for present perfect, **past per** for past perfect, or **fut per** for future perfect.

EXAMPLE: The orchestra and band *have begun* plans for the music festival.
(pres per)

11 Surely the bell *rang* a long time ago. *(past)*

12 Joe *will run* in the mile race next Wednesday. *(fut)*

13 The river *has risen* several feet within the last hour. *(pres per)*

14 They *have sat* there on that bench for more than an hour. *(pres per)*

15 *Speak* to Ms. Williams about the price of the tickets for the play. *(pres)*

16 She *will not have finished* her story by this afternoon. *(fut per)*

17 Harold and I *swam* across Round Lake yesterday afternoon. *(past)*

18 The workers *will have laid* the last brick by tomorrow night. *(fut per)*

19 Don *had not written* his application letter at noon today. *(past per)*

20 The high school rock band *will play* for us at the school dance tomorrow evening. *(fut)*

Plain English Handbook, 190–196, 207.

SCORE _____ (Top Score 30)

LESSON 13

Forming Tenses/1

In each sentence write the correct form of the verb indicated in the parentheses.

EXAMPLE: (ring — past perfect)   The bell ___*had rung*___ before I opened the door.

1 (swim — past)   The girls ___swam___ to the deep end of the pool.

2 (see — past)   Barry ___saw___ the Veterans' parade yesterday.

3 (lie — past perfect)   We ___had lain___ on the grass to rest awhile.

4 (do — past)   Robert ___did___ his very best to win his race.

5 (come — future perfect)   Jack ___will have come___ before ten o'clock tonight.

6 (swing — past)   My cousin ___swung___ her bat carelessly.

7 (bring — past)   Neither boy ___brought___ his own pencil.

8 (do — present perfect)   Ann ___has done___ the work for us.

9 (drink — present perfect)   They ___have drunk___ all the milk in the refrigerator.

10 (blow — past)   The wind ___blew___ hard all day yesterday.

11 (know — future)   She ___will know___ the results of her exam before lunch.

12 (lie — past)   The traveler ___lay___ down in the shade of that linden tree.

13 (eat — past perfect)   Toni ___had eaten___ her lunch before we arrived.

14 (break — past perfect)   We heard that he ___had broken___ the school record.

15 (ring — past)   Class had started before the bell ___rang___.

16 (give — past)   My brother ___gave___ me this sweater for Christmas.

17 (throw — past perfect)   Mrs. Young ___had thrown___ the small fish back into the lake.

18 (lie — present)   That lazy kitten ___lies___ on the couch every day.

19 (shake — future perfect)   Jim ___will have shaken___ the smaller rugs before he leaves.

20 (go — past perfect)   Catrina ___had gone___ when we arrived at her house.

Plain English Handbook, 190–196, 204, 207, 216, 217.

21

Spelling List/2

deceive	inquiry	industrial	awkward	juvenile
precious	partial	acres	experience	strict
science	confer	relatives	lecture	harmony
neither	glimpse	existed	solemn	apogee
neighbors	advertisement	actual	adjust	depot
species	interfere	various	wisdom	university
ancient	luncheon	fission	theme	journal
young	maintenance	sacred	pierced	equipment

SCORE _____ (Top Score 20)

Forming Tenses/2

In each sentence write the correct tense form indicated in the parentheses.

EXAMPLE: (take — present perfect) The coach _____*has taken*_____ the track team to the meet.

1 (rise — past) The unhappy defendant _____rose_____ to her feet reluctantly.

2 (go — present perfect) Are you sure the boys _____have gone_____ to the game?

3 (sink — present perfect) The sun _____has sunk_____ from sight behind the mountains.

4 (sit — past perfect) They _____had sat_____ at the airport for over an hour.

5 (set — past) Rich very carefully _____set_____ the Chinese vase on the table.

6 (know — past) Tish _____knew_____ the answer, but she was not called upon in class.

7 (rise — future perfect) The river _____will have risen_____ a foot by this evening.

8 (shake — present perfect) I'm afraid Tom _____has shaken_____ that tree too hard.

9 (rise — past perfect) The moon _____had risen_____ before we sailed the boat to shore.

10 (sit — present) We often just _____sit_____ beside the pool and dangle our feet.

11 (ride — present perfect) Donna _____has ridden_____ her horse in many shows by now.

12 (sing — past perfect) The seniors _____had sung_____ many school songs that we had never heard.

13 (speak — present perfect) Kate _____has spoken_____ with the principal about the matter.

14 (swim — past perfect) Jan _____had swum_____ across the pool twice before I dived in.

15 (write — present perfect) Sue _____has written_____ a magazine article about rock music.

16 (tear — past perfect) The wind _____had torn_____ the small sailboat from its moorings.

17 (do — future perfect) Bill _____will have done_____ his lessons by the time we are to leave.

18 (grow — present perfect) Jill _____has grown_____ three inches since we last saw her.

19 (sink — past perfect) The *Titanic* _____had sunk_____ before the *Carpathia* could reach her.

20 (throw — past) Jo _____threw_____ her sweater over her shoulder and hurried to the court.

22

Plain English Handbook, 190–196, 204, 207–209, 216, 217.

Activity: Review carefully the principal parts of the verbs listed in *Plain English Handbook,* 204. If you know the principal parts of a verb, you will be able to form any tense easily. Write the principal parts of each of the verbs given above.

SCORE _____ (Top Score 20)

Conjugation of the Verb *To Give*

On each line write the correct form for the conjugation of the verb *to give* in the active voice, indicative mood.

Present Tense

SINGULAR		PLURAL	
1 I give		1 we give	
2 you give		2 you give	
3 he gives		3 they give	

Past Tense

1 I gave		1 we gave	
2 you gave		2 you gave	
3 he gave		3 they gave	

Future Tense

1 I shall give		1 we shall give	
2 you will give		2 you will give	
3 he will give		3 they will give	

Present Perfect Tense

1 I have given		1 we have given	
2 you have given		2 you have given	
3 he has given		3 they have given	

Past Perfect Tense

1 I had given		1 we had given	
2 you had given		2 you had given	
3 he had given		3 they had given	

Future Perfect Tense

1 I shall have given		1 we shall have given	
2 you will have given		2 you will have given	
3 he will have given		3 they will have given	

23

Plain English Handbook, 183, 184, 186, 187, 190–196, 204, 205, 207.

Activity: On a separate sheet of paper, write the conjugation of *to give* in the progressive form (209). Write the conjugation of *to give* in the passive voice, indicative mood (185, 208).

SCORE _____ (Top Score 36)

Forming Tenses/3

A verb is given at the beginning of each group of sentences below. In each sentence of the group write the tense form of this verb called for in the parentheses. The **p** following the tense indication means that the form is to be passive; otherwise all forms are to be active.

EXAMPLES: break

(past perfect) The wind _____*had broken*_____ three windows.

(present perfect — p) Three windows _____*have been broken*_____ by the wind.

give

1 (past) Are you sure that he _____gave_____ you the correct number of tickets?

2 (future) Larry _____will give_____ you your tickets by noon tomorrow.

3 (past — p) The prize _____was given_____ to the person who sold the most tickets.

4 (present perfect) Pat's mother _____has given_____ us an order for 30 tickets.

come

5 (future perfect) They _____will have come_____ to the meeting by seven.

6 (past) The boys _____came_____ early to help clean up the clubroom.

7 (present perfect) Some girls _____have come_____ to help us set up the chairs.

lie

8 (present) Our big black cat often _____lies_____ on that window seat.

9 (past perfect) One day we found that he _____had lain_____ on the mantel all night.

10 (past) We _____lay_____ on the lawn and watched him try to catch a blowing leaf.

11 (present perfect) That lazy cat _____has lain_____ there and watched us all day.

raise

12 (past) The chairperson quickly _____raised_____ the question himself.

13 (past perfect — p) A discussion _____had been raised_____ about the last motion.

rise

14 (past perfect) Ken _____had risen_____ from treasurer to chairperson in a short time.

15 (past) The students _____rose_____ to their feet when the president entered.

16 (present perfect) The chairperson _____has risen_____ to introduce the speaker.

sit

17 (present) That old man _____sits_____ near me in my pottery class.

18 (past perfect) He _____had sat_____ there often before we ever noticed him.

19 (past) We _____sat_____ in the boat while Jim rowed it around the pond.

20 (present perfect — p) The bench _____has been sat_____ on by many different people.

Plain English Handbook, 184, 185, 190–196, 204, 207, 208, 216, 217.

Activity: Write the principal parts of each of the six verbs used in this lesson. *Plain English Handbook,* 204.

24

Forming Tenses/4

A verb is given at the beginning of each group of sentences below. In each sentence of the group write the tense form of this verb called for in the parentheses. The **p** following the tense indication means that the form is to be passive; otherwise all forms are to be active.

EXAMPLES: lay

(past)   Sam _____*laid*_____ the silverware on the table.

(present perfect — p)   Many stones _____*have been laid*_____ for a rock garden.

speak

1 (past perfect)   I wish you _____had spoken_____ with me about this matter.

2 (past — p)   The words _____were spoken_____ very distinctly by the radio announcer.

3 (present perfect)   That man certainly _____has spoken_____ plainly enough.

swim

4 (future perfect)   She _____will have swum_____ across the pool four times without a rest.

5 (present perfect)   All the campers _____have swum_____ across the lake already.

6 (past)   Susan and I _____swam_____ until we were **exhausted.**

7 (past perfect)   Bob _____had swum_____ in many other contests before this one.

sing

8 (present perfect — p)   That old song _____has been sung_____ many times.

9 (past perfect)   James _____had sung_____ his solo before you came into the room.

10 (past — p)   The big soprano part _____was sung_____ by Helen Erickson.

see

11 (future perfect)   He _____will have seen_____ the principal before he sees us.

12 (past)   Barbara and I _____saw_____ the Mayan art exhibit yesterday.

13 (past perfect — p)   The stranger _____had been seen_____ by several of the boys.

go

14 (present perfect)   All the students _____have gone_____ to today's game.

15 (future perfect)   Freda _____will have gone_____ before our plane arrives.

16 (past perfect)   I wish I _____had gone_____ to the horse show with the others.

do

17 (past)   Betty _____did_____ excellent work in school last year.

18 (present perfect)   The girls _____have done_____ their jobs very quickly.

19 (past perfect)   I wish we _____had done_____ our work before the party.

20 (present perfect — p)   Most of the planning _____has been done_____ by Louise.

Plain English Handbook, 174, 175, 190–196, 204, 207, 208, 216.

Activity: In original sentences use the verbs given above in all six tenses.

SCORE _____ (Top Score 20)

25

Using the Progressive Form of Verbs

In each sentence write the correct progressive tense form indicated in the parentheses.

EXAMPLE: (blow — present perfect)   The storm _____*has been blowing*_____ violently for an hour.

1 (swim — future)   If we hurry we _____will be swimming_____ in the lake soon.

2 (rise — past)   The moon _____was rising_____ over the hills as we left the party.

3 (go — present)   The students _____are going_____ to their classes now.

4 (do — present perfect)   Anita _____has been doing_____ her work well this term.

5 (see — future)   We _____will be seeing_____ Carol and Chuck very soon.

6 (sing — past)   The glee club _____was singing_____ with only piano accompaniment.

7 (ring — past)   The bell for class _____was ringing_____ when I left home.

8 (lie — past)   Your coat _____was lying_____ on the chair when I last saw it.

9 (ride — present)   Tony _____is riding_____ his new motor scooter today.

10 (set — present)   Mary _____is setting_____ a good example for the others.

11 (raise — past perfect)   Tom _____had been raising_____ the windows for Mrs. James.

12 (drive — future)   Rita _____will be driving_____ her new sports coupe to the lake.

13 (write — present perfect)   Ellen _____has been writing_____ her theme for tomorrow.

14 (give — past)   The chairperson _____was giving_____ his report when they entered.

15 (lie — present perfect)   That book _____has been lying_____ on the floor all day.

16 (come — past perfect)   Until last week Joe _____had been coming_____ to school early.

17 (lay — present)   The workers _____are laying_____ the foundation for the new school.

18 (lay — past perfect)   The mason _____had been laying_____ the bricks for our fireplace.

19 (sit — future)   They _____will be sitting_____ there, just as they are now, when we return.

20 (speak — past perfect)   Ruth _____had been speaking_____ to the class when we came into the room.

Plain English Handbook, 190–196, 204, 207–212, 216, 217.

Activity: Write a note inviting a friend to a picnic that you are giving next weekend. Be sure to include all the necessary information. *Plain English Handbook,* 617.

SCORE _____ (Top Score 20)

Verb Agreement

In each sentence write the correct verb form from within the parentheses.

EXAMPLE: (is/are) Every one of the Coopers ____*is*____ blond.

1 (am/is) It is I who ____am____ to blame for the unfortunate error.

2 (is/are) Ham and eggs ____is____ a favorite American dish.

3 (was/were) Our glee club ____was____ very popular this year.

4 (is/are) One of our exchange students ____is____ from Mexico.

5 (are/is) A large and a small boat ____are____ on the lake now.

6 (Are/Is) ____Are____ Bob and his cousin going skating with us?

7 (is/are) Neither Joan nor Miss Dale ____is____ here right now.

8 (was/were) The director, not the players, ____was____ responsible.

9 (were/was) Sixty dollars ____was____ paid for the new art room equipment.

10 (was/were) Neither the coach nor the players ____were____ in the locker room.

11 (don't/doesn't) The teacher ____doesn't____ permit the class to get noisy.

12 (come/comes) Here ____come____ the members from the Honor Society meeting.

13 (is/are) The number of sophomores ____is____ unusually large this year.

14 (was/were) Each of the girls ____was____ doing her best to win the game.

15 (was/were) The director, as well as the actors, ____was____ grateful for his praise.

16 (is/are) Each of the students ____is____ selling tickets for Saturday's dance.

17 (are/is) A great number of students ____are____ planning to go on to college.

18 (is/are) Dotty is one of those persons who ____are____ always pleasant.

19 (is/are) It is one of those decisions that ____are____ always difficult to make.

20 (was/were) Plenty of meat ____was____ provided for the school barbecue by a local rancher.

Plain English Handbook, 197, 236–242, 244, 246, 261.

Activity: The merchandise which you ordered in Lesson 8 has been delivered to you, but one article is defective. Write to the department store, carefully explaining the unsatisfactory condition of the article. Be sure to plan your letter before you write it. *Plain English Handbook,* 610.

Spelling List/3

happier	concession	response	literature	fusion
accomplish	spacecraft	particularly	distribute	toboggans
experiments	rebellion	investigate	benefited	handful
usually	manual	lift-off	description	advertising
issue	introduction	volume	witness	interview
accompany	expressing	expensive	occasion	vacancy
referred	scarcity	brilliant	demonstration	postpone
opportunity	endurance	superintendent	discuss	religious

SCORE _____ (Top Score 20)

27

Confusing Verbs

In each sentence write the correct forms of the verbs given.

EXAMPLE: rise, raise

The cost of living must ___*rise*___ before sellers can ___*raise*___ prices for their merchandise.

sit, set

1 We must have ___set___ out at least twenty plants before we ___sat___ down to rest.

2 Mom ___sat___ in her favorite chair, and ___set___ her book and glasses on the end table beside her.

3 We ___sat___ down at the table, and the waiter ___set___ a menu in front of each of us.

4 Mother ___set___ the turkey on the table while we ___sat___ and admired it.

5 Don and Jack have ___sat___ there ever since we ___set___ that bench in the shade.

6 Ray ___set___ a bowl of meat before the dog, but the dog just ___sat___ and looked at it.

7 After we had ___set___ the hurdles in place, we ___sat___ on the bench with Tom.

lie, lay

8 Your coat is still ___lying___ on the same chair where you ___laid___ it.

9 The banner is ___lying___ on the ground, but I did not ___lay___ it there.

10 The dog will ___lie___ down close to where his master is now ___lying___.

11 While I was ___lying___ on the beach, a black cocker spaniel came and ___lay___ beside me.

12 Where did you ___lay___ the book? It must still be ___lying___ there.

13 We'll let the new carpet ___lie___ here until someone can ___lay___ it for us.

14 The money has ___lain___ on the mantelpiece since you ___laid___ it there last week.

rise, raise

15 We should have ___risen___ when the judge ___rose___ from the bench.

16 Tom had already ___risen___ to speak before Don ___raised___ a new objection.

17 If you ___raise___ the oven heat now, your cake will not ___rise___ well.

18 You may ___raise___ the window if the wind has not ___risen___.

19 The temperature was ___rising___ rapidly when we ___rose___ to start on our hike.

20 The speaker ___raised___ his hand, and the audience ___rose___ to its feet.

Plain English Handbook, 190–196, 204, 207–212, 217.

SCORE _____ (Top Score 40)

LESSON 21

Using Verbs/1

Cross out each incorrect verb and write the correct form above it. If there is no incorrect verb, write **C** before the sentence.

             gone
EXAMPLE: They had ~~went~~ only a short way when they had a flat tire.   (204)

1 Are you sure that it is I who ~~is~~ *am* to blame? (249)

2 ~~Can~~ *May* Helen and I borrow your record player, Pedro? (218)

3 Jaime went home and ~~done~~ *did* his homework. (204, 216)

4 Were you at the game when Tom ~~seen~~ *saw* you? (260, 204, 216)

5 Each of the players ~~were~~ *was* making every effort to win. (242)

6 We found that five miles ~~were~~ *was* too long a distance to walk. (245)

7 I could ~~of~~ *have* sat there an hour listening to his talk. (230, 217)

8 It is one of those subjects that ~~is~~ *are* always interesting. (241)

9 If she offers me the job, I promise I will ~~except~~ *accept* it. (220, 228)

10 ~~Was~~ *Were* you appointed chairperson of the art committee? (260, 185)

11 Gwen says that she has already ~~did~~ *done* her assigned book report. (204, 216)

12 My little brother ~~growed~~ *grew* about three inches last year. (204)

13 The coach has done his best to ~~learn~~ *teach* James to throw good passes. (216, 227)

14 Did anyone in Biblical times believe that the earth ~~was~~ *is* round? (251)

15 Neither the book nor the pencils ~~is~~ *are* lying on the table now. (238, 217)

16 There ~~was~~ *were* four students nominated for the presidency of the club. (239)

17 We should ~~raise~~ *rise* to our feet when Judge Trowbridge comes in. (204, 216, 217)

C 18 The coach, no less than the players, is to blame for what they did. (236, 216)

19 The bracelet that Terry ~~give~~ *gave* me should be lying on the table. (204, 216, 217)

20 We came early, but you had already ~~went~~ *gone* to the skating rink. (203, 216)

21 If I ~~was~~ *were* only a little older, Mother would teach me to drive our car. (256, 227)

22 Have you seen the book I ~~lay~~ *laid* on the desk a few minutes ago? (204, 216, 217)

23 We had ~~set~~ *sat* there for fifteen minutes before the play began. (204, 217)

24 A great number of trees ~~was~~ *were* broken in the hurricane last summer. (244, 185, 204)

25 I am sure that one of the girls ~~have~~ *has* taken the tickets that Al gave us. (246, 185, 204)

Numbers in parentheses refer to *Plain English Handbook.*

29

SCORE _____ (Top Score 25)

Using Verbs/2

Cross out each incorrect verb and write the correct form above it. If there is no incorrect verb, write C before the sentence.

EXAMPLE: There ~~was~~ *were* seven passengers waiting at the bus stop when I arrived.

1 Bob had not ~~wrote~~ *written* his paper when I saw him this morning.

2 One of the new players ~~are~~ *is* here, but the coach has already gone home.

3 We ~~drunk~~ *drank* the lemonade before we started our tennis match.

4 Hank ~~brung~~ *brought* the tickets to the hockey game to us yesterday.

5 I ~~begun~~ *began* typing my story on conservation right after breakfast.

6 The starting bell has rung, but Jack has not ~~came~~ *come* to class yet.

7 If the book is ~~tore~~ *torn*, we should report it to the librarian.

8 All the girls ~~done~~ *did* their best, but they were defeated.

9 This catcher's mitt was almost ~~wore~~ *worn* out when Hal gave it to me.

10 As soon as Tim had eaten his breakfast, he ~~run~~ *ran* to catch the school bus.

11 The doorbell had ~~rang~~ *rung* some five times before anyone heard it.

30

12 There ~~was~~ *were* two children with Larry when we saw him at the new art museum.

13 All the girls have ~~ate~~ *eaten* lunch, and some of them have already gone to class.

14 Paul ~~don't~~ *doesn't* like that subject, though he has done excellent work in it.

15 If they had ~~began~~ *begun* serious practice earlier, they would have done better.

16 After we had driven a short way, we ~~seen~~ *saw* that we had taken the wrong turning.

C 17 The boys have finished their sandwiches, but they have not eaten dessert.

18 The boys have done the decorating of the gym, and most of them have ~~went~~ *gone* home.

19 Charles ~~give~~ *gave* me this book before he hurried off to his English class.

20 The track team has done very well, but it has not ~~broke~~ *broken* any records.

Plain English Handbook, 190–197, 204, 207–208, 216, 239, 246.

Activity: Pronunciation must be correct if we are to be understood. Section 675 in *Plain English Handbook* lists words which are frequently mispronounced. Using a dictionary, study the marking of each of these words until you can pronounce each correctly. The section on pronunciation, pages 11a to 24a, at the front of *Webster's Intermediate Dictionary* gives complete information on the subject.

SCORE _____ (Top Score 20)

Using Verbs/3

To complete each of the following sentences insert the correct form of the verb within the parentheses.

EXAMPLE: Neither Jill nor I _____*was*_____ (were/was) at the airport when he arrived.

1 More than two-thirds of the students _____were_____ (were/was) at the meeting.

2 Lorrie flies in jet planes often, but she has not _____flown_____ (flew/flown) in a helicopter.

3 Most of the civilian airliners flying now _____are_____ (are/is) jets and, there _____are_____ (are/is) now in service the giant 747's.

4 Each of the jets _____is_____ (are/is) powered by kerosenelike fuel.

5 When the storm _____came_____ (come/came) close, he _____ran_____ (ran/run) down to the cellar.

6 Either Miss Fields or one of the administrators _____is_____ (are/is) to go to the meeting.

7 Tim and I _____saw_____ (seen/saw) Jan during halftime at the football game.

8 When I saw Pete yesterday, he _____gave_____ (give/gave) me this message for you.

9 We had _____gone_____ (went/gone) to the play before Dave came with the tickets.

10 Jim had never been in an airplane, yet he _____began_____ (begun/began) to write about one.

11 Ms. James poured a glass of water and the small boy _____drank_____ (drunk/drank) it thirstily.

12 Plenty of activities _____were_____ (were/was) planned for the class exhibit.

13 The first U. S. civilian jet liner was _____flown_____ (flew/flown) from New York to Paris.

14 Emilia is one of those girls who _____are_____ (are/is) always very assertive.

15 Neither the coach nor the player _____is_____ (are/is) to be blamed for the error.

16 The record for the high jump was _____broken_____ (broke/broken) by someone from our school.

17 _____Are_____ (Are/Is) the committee ready to hand in their votes?

18 One of the principal members of the cast _____was_____ (was/were) sick on opening night.

Plain English Handbook, 197, 204, 207, 208, 216, 237–244, 246.

Activity: Choose a topic and write a short theme. The topic may be developed by means of details, examples, comparison or contrast, cause and effect, or a combination of any two or more of these methods. *Plain English Handbook,* 544–545.

SCORE _____ (Top Score 20)

31

LESSON 24
Using Verbals

In each sentence write the correct expression from within the parentheses.

EXAMPLE: (Tom/Tom's) We were proud of _____Tom's_____ winning the high dive.

1 (having started/starting) Janet has been working a month, _____having started_____ the first of May.

2 (me/I) Harry took him to be _____me_____.

3 (she/her) Joe thought me to be _____her_____.

4 (I/me) Luisa was thought to be _____I_____.

5 (he/him) You were thought to be _____he_____.

6 (he/him) Were you believed to be _____he_____?

7 (Who/Whom) _____Whom_____ did you take me to be?

8 (him/his) We encouraged _____his_____ entering the next contest.

9 (you/your) I am delighted at _____your_____ learning to sail your new boat.

10 (she/her) The teacher must have taken me to be _____her_____.

11 (to work/working) To play is as important as _____to work_____.

12 (me/my) He was disappointed at _____my_____ losing the last race.

13 (us/our) Did the janitor report _____our_____ writing on the walls?

14 (Kim/Kim's) Are you in favor of _____Kim's_____ representing the class tomorrow?

15 (them/their) The explorer told us about _____their_____ discovering Crystal Cave.

16 (you/your) I think that _____your_____ coming with us is a very good idea.

17 (playing/to play) I think playing tennis is better exercise than _____playing_____ golf.

18 (departing/having departed) She has been gone a month, _____having departed_____ on June 20.

19 (money was saved/we saved money) By taking the bus, _____we saved money_____.

20 (having met/meeting) Jane and I are no longer strangers, _____having met_____ one another last week.

Plain English Handbook, 198–201, 264, 270, 274, 450.

Activity: Making a speech gives excellent practice in using good English and in securing poise and confidence before a group. During the school year numerous occasions offer opportunities for speech activities. During fire prevention week, at Christmas time or at Thanksgiving, or during a charity drive, occasions arise which call for speeches. Write a speech urging your classmates to support some worthy cause or expressing the true spirit of a holiday. *Plain English Handbook*, 643.

SCORE _____ (Top Score 20)

LESSON 25
Reviewing Verbs

Cross out each incorrect verb and write its correct form above it.

saw
EXAMPLE: When Barbara and I looked at our basement, we ~~seen~~ a fine place for a recreation room.

drew
1 Last week, Barbara and I ~~drawed~~ plans for a basement recreation room.

done
2 Mom and Dad hoped they had ~~did~~ the right thing by letting us decorate it ourselves.

began
3 Before we ~~begun~~ painting the room, we measured the walls and floor.

knew
4 We ~~knowed~~ exactly how much paint we would need before we started.

grew
5 Images of an architect's dream ~~growed~~ in our minds as we painted.

eaten
6 After we had ~~ate~~ lunch, we hurried back to the basement.

broken
7 Reb, our dog, had ~~broke~~ our only lamp.

stuck
8 Some of his fur had ~~sticked~~ on the newly painted walls.

given
9 We thought we could cover it with some posters Cousin Arlene had ~~give~~ us.

ridden
10 To make matters worse, our little brother had ~~rode~~ through on his tricycle; we now have a striped floor!

taken
11 I should have ~~took~~ them both outside and locked the doors before we started.

gave
12 On the next day we ~~give~~ most of our attention to bookshelves.

driven
13 Mom had ~~drove~~ us to the lumberyard to get wood for the shelves.

drove
14 We started to make the bookshelves, but we ~~drived~~ the nails in incorrectly.

chosen
15 I wondered if Barbara ever regretted that she had ~~chose~~ to begin this project.

began
16 After several hours of sawing and hammering, I certainly ~~begun~~ to wonder why we had ever wanted a rec room!

saw
17 The do-it-yourself bookshelves we ~~seen~~ in a magazine seemed so easy to do.

sung
18 We could have ~~sang~~ for joy when we had to stop for dinner.

done
19 Dad said he should have ~~did~~ some carpentry work with us to give us practice using tools.

chosen
20 Maybe we should have ~~chose~~ an easier project.

Plain English Handbook, 190–196, 204, 216.

33

Spelling List/4

annual	desirous	guitars	capsule	belief
possession	pamphlet	accurate	tournament	assume
institute	urgent	elevator	crisis	whistle
electricity	initiation	ridiculous	portion	affect
aviation	element	arctic	sought	temperamental
variety	unfortunate	omitted	expression	altitude
explanation	access	establish	interruption	agriculture
insurance	preparations	schedule	title	sacrifice

SCORE _____ (Top Score 20)

Reviewing Verb Agreement

Cross out each incorrect verb and write the correct form above it. If there is no incorrect verb, write **C** before the sentence.

were
EXAMPLE: There ~~was~~ twelve girls in the group, but only four were sophomores.   (239)

were
1 If I ~~was~~ king, I would declare every Monday a holiday.   (256)

doesn't
2 It seems that Bob ~~don't~~ know which of the girls is leader.   (197, 246)

Don't
3 ~~Doesn't~~ the hat and jacket lying on that chair belong to Rolando?   (197)

are
4 A large number of students ~~is~~ going to the table tennis match today.   (244)

was
5 We thought that twenty dollars ~~were~~ too much for that old chair.   (245)

C 6 The number of traffic accidents over Memorial Day was very large.   (244)

is
7 One of the boys ~~are~~ here, but neither of the girls has come yet.   (246, 242)

was
8 If Jill ~~were at~~ the meeting, neither she nor Don has said so.   (257, 237)

are
9   Helen is one of those people who ~~is~~ always very competitive.   (197, 241)

is
10 There were few ancients who believed that the earth ~~was~~ round.   (239, 251)

were
11 Everyone of the girls now talks as if she ~~was~~ acting a part in a play.   (242, 258)

was
12 Jenny, as well as Sue, ~~were~~ here; but there were others to come.   (236, 239)

were
13 A black and a blue car ~~was~~ parked in front of Jim's house yesterday.   (248)

were
14 If I ~~was~~ you, I'd ask one of those clerks who are always so pleasant.   (256, 241)

were
15 You ~~was~~ the first winner, but neither of the others has been chosen.   (260, 242)

are
16 There ~~is~~ two volunteers to work at the booth, but one of them is not here.   (239, 246)

thinks
17 Each of the columnists ~~think~~ that our team is sure to win the soccer trophy.   (242, 240)

is
18 There are many good desserts, but peaches and cream ~~are~~ my favorite.   (239, 247)

has
19 Neither Kay nor Dan ~~have joined~~ the club, but Jean and Lou are members.   (237, 247)

has
20 Neither the typists nor the secretary ~~have~~ been here since you were elected chairperson.   (238, 260)

have
21 Neither Ed nor the newcomers ~~has~~ sent the money to the treasurer.   (237, 247)

think
22 The actors, not the director, ~~thinks~~ the drama club is ready for the play.   (261, 240)

has
23 The jury ~~have~~ made a decision, and everyone is eager to hear the verdict.   (240, 242)

have
24 Kay doesn't know that a number of her friends ~~has~~ been invited to the party.   (197, 244)

C 25 Neither Hank nor Nina thinks that two hundred dollars is too much for that old car.   (237, 245)

34

Substantives, Modifiers, and Connectives

This test parallels, in content, Inventory 3, page 107.

I. *Using Substantives*
(Lessons 27–32, 37–42)   30 Points

Cross out each incorrect noun or pronoun and write the correct form above it.

EXAMPLE: Joan and he have brought a picnic lunch for ~~we~~ *us* club members.

1 Joe and I have two ~~sister-in-laws~~ *sisters-in-law* now.

2 Is it he ~~whom~~ *who* you think is taller than I?

3 Who did he say sent Hal and ~~I~~ *me* the tickets?

4 Jackie and she are much younger than Bob and ~~him~~ *he*.

5 All we boys but George and ~~he~~ *him* will go to the county fair.

6 How can I find Dr. ~~Lane's~~ *Lane* and Dr. Sullivan's office?

7 I am quite sure it was ~~him~~ *he* who came with Dorothy and her.

8 Margarita and I used two ~~cupsful~~ *cupfuls* of sugar in the cake.

9 All ~~us~~ *we* students think it was he whom we saw with her.

10 Could it have been ~~her~~ *she* whom you saw with Jack and him?

11 Was it ~~him~~ *he* who made the plans for the meeting of us boys?

12 It must have been ~~them~~ *they* who brought these books for Jim and me.

13 Was it Gayle and she who took Paul and ~~he~~ *him* to their club dance?

14 James and ~~her~~ *she* are the two who are to go with Suzanne and me.

15 Aunt Grace gave Louise and ~~I~~ *me* enough chairs for all of us cousins and our guests.

16 The jacket hanging on that hook looks like my ~~brother's-in-law~~ *brother-in-law's*.

17 Was it she and Luis whom we saw at the theater with Vic and ~~she~~ *her*?

18 Was it he whom you asked to bring the costumes down to ~~we~~ *us* actors?

19 Are Miss Martinez and she going with ~~we~~ *us* girls to the newspaper office?

20 Every girl on the crew will do ~~their~~ *her* best to help us win the race.

21 Could it have been ~~them~~ *they* who sent us the newspaper clippings?

22 ~~Whomever~~ *Whoever* is elected will take office next September.

23 This is ~~somebody's else~~ *somebody else's* book, because I am sure that it is not mine.

24 Hugo and she have made sketches of all of us students except Dot and ~~she~~ *her*.

                                         we
25 All ~~us~~ students should encourage our team to maintain its reputation.
                                   boys'
26 Hank works in the ~~boy's~~ shop at Jordan's, and Judy is in the hardware department.
                                          who
27 He is a newspaper columnist ~~whom~~ we think is a friend to all us students.
                                               her
28 Each girl in the class should take ~~their~~ problems to the counselor, Ms. Williams.
                                            she
29 Bill and I think that Bess and ~~her~~ will help us players get the tennis courts in order.
                                  moose
30 Jan thinks that ~~mooses~~ are the most ungainly and homely animals in the United States.

II. *Using Modifiers and Connectives*

(Lessons 33–36, 40–42)   20 Points

Cross out each incorrect adjective, adverb, preposition, or conjunction and write the correct form above it.

                                        beautiful
EXAMPLE: The mountains looked ~~beautifully~~ in the early morning sunlight.

                                             bitter
1 The pineapple looked good, but it tasted ~~bitterly~~.
                                  unless
2 The team cannot win ~~except~~ it practices regularly.
                                                  well
3 Tom has a small build, but he plays football ~~good~~.
                bad
4 Ann feels ~~badly~~ because she spoke so rudely yesterday.
                       any (or omit not*)*
5 There is not ~~no~~ reason for her treating us so indifferently.
                 somewhat
6 Roberto feels ~~some~~ better today, but he still feels bad.
                                   any (or omit not*)*
7 Jack played very well, but he was not ~~no~~ match for Bill.
                               fewer
8 We catchers surely make ~~less~~ mistakes on the baseball field now.
                                          surely
9 Although he is the youngest of the three, he ~~sure~~ plays well.
                                          behind
10 When we came into the room, Ken was sitting ~~in back of~~ the desk.
                                                   differently
11 We could have done this more quickly if we had done it ~~different~~.
                                               better
12 Although Cathy is not nearly so large as Mona, she is the ~~best~~ athlete.
                                                anywhere
13 Jean is somewhat upset because she cannot find her jacket ~~anywheres~~.
                  very (or really*)*
14 The stories are ~~real~~ interesting, but they are not carefully written.
                       that
15 I read in the paper ~~where~~ the weather is to be somewhat colder today.
              taller
16 Nan was the ~~tallest~~ of my two cousins who went skating with Beth and me.
                        from
17 Your pen is different ~~than~~ Bob's or mine, but it is the best of the three.
                                                   within
18 Maria, the older of the two sisters, hopes to finish the course ~~inside of~~ two years.
                     from
19 Although Ed and I are twins, we differ ~~with~~ each other in looks and personality.
                     from
20 This car is different ~~than~~ the others, for the steering wheel is on the right side.

SCORE _____ (Top Score 50)

LESSON 27

Using Nouns

Cross out each noun used incorrectly and write the correct form above it. If there is no incorrect noun, write **C** before the sentence.

lives
EXAMPLE: Many ~~lifes~~ have been saved by the discovery of penicillin.   (82)

oxen
1 Are ~~oxes~~ still used as farm animals in India?   (85)

C 2 The farmers in the valleys grow many potatoes each year.   (81, 78)

C 3 Weren't you surprised at Kay's refusing the part of Juliet?   (127)

deer
4 We brought back two ~~deers~~ from our hunting trip in Wisconsin.   (89)

jockeys
5 It is very important that all ~~jockies~~ remain light in weight.   (81)

Jan's
6 ~~Jan~~ and Al's hands were dirty after they had changed the tire.   (125)

father-in-law's
7 Fred is going to take his ~~father's-in-law~~ new car to the picnic.   (123)

sisters-in-law
8 Margie and her two ~~sister-in-laws~~ are spending a week in Chicago.   (86)

bucketfuls
9 It required twenty-five ~~bucketsful~~ of sand to fill Tim's sandbox.   (87)

roofs
10 The ~~rooves~~ of many of the old houses in Holland were made of tile.   (83)

Mary's
11 ~~Marys~~ sisters-in-law gave her two new charms for her bracelet.   (117, 86)

girl's
12 The ~~girls~~' coat was lying on the ground as she played ball.   (120)

cries
13 The baby-sitter was alarmed when she heard the children's ~~crys~~.   (122, 80)

geese
14 Instead of turkey, we are going to have two ~~gooses~~ this Thanksgiving.   (84)

turkeys
15 Mr. Jackson will furnish the ~~turkies~~ for the award banquet.   (81)

Pat's
16 We are so pleased about ~~Pat~~ winning the scholarship to the university.   (127)

somebody else's
17 Julia, you will have to use ~~somebody's else~~ book until you find yours.   (126)

girls'
18 The five ~~girl's~~ mural was among the winners of the modern art contest.   (121)

radios
19 Randee took both ~~radioes~~ and the record player to the repair shop today.   (79)

i's
20 Dotty, your handwriting would be much neater if you would dot your ~~is~~'.   (88)

halves
21 I told Tom and Jo that we would meet them between the ~~halfs~~ of the game.   (82)

Brown
22 Mark bought a new sport coat at ~~Brown's~~ and King's Shop on Tenth Street.   (124)

parents'
23 The ~~parent's~~ group is meeting upstairs, and the teenagers' group is down here.   (121)

children's
24 During her vacation, Barb is working in the ~~childrens~~' shop at the Plaza.   (122)

C 25 My aunt has charge of the women's department in Lee and Jones' Shop.   (122, 120, 124)

SCORE _____ (Top Score 25)

Using Pronouns

If the italicized pronoun is correctly used, draw a line beneath it. If it is incorrectly used, write the correct form above it.

EXAMPLE: Joanna will go to the beach with Sue and *she*. (153)
[her written above "she"]

1 Aren't Lee and Jody both much younger than *her*? (148)
[she written above "her"]

2 Steve and *them* should be here soon with our picnic lunch. (149)
[they written above "them"]

3 Sue is growing so fast that she must be nearly as tall as *me*. (148)
[I written above "me"]

4 That howling dog wandering around the woods must have lost *it's* way. (146)
[its written above "it's"]

5 Send <u>whoever</u> will be able to deliver the message the quickest. (161)

6 I believe that Joe and he looked for *we* joggers in the wrong park. (157)
[us written above "we"]

7 Roger and *her* will give their committee reports at the next meeting. (149)
[she written above "her"]

8 The director gave Carl and *I* directions about our second-act entrance. (154)
[me written above "I"]

9 Janet and Ned had planned to sit near Neta and *I*, but we got separated. (153)
[me written above "I"]

10 Everyone in the class but Carlotta and *she* has a job during the summer. (156)
[her written above "she"]

11 I am sure that Mrs. Turner will have enough room in her car for *we* girls. (157)
[us written above "we"]

12 Julie is the aspirant <u>who</u> we believe will play the part of Lady Macbeth best. (159)

13 Do you think that we will be able to find Mark and *he* in this huge crowd? (153)
[him written above "he"]

14 Alice brought the tickets and the cashbox to the booth for Louise and *I*. (153)
[me written above "I"]

15 Is it *him* and Rose who are to represent Central High in the swimming meet? (152)
[he written above "him"]

16 We will welcome *whoever* the principal chooses to be our graduation speaker. (162)
[whomever written above "whoever"]

17 Was it *them* who decided that Barry would be a good candidate? (152)
[they written above "them"]

18 All *us* students on the Student Council voted in favor of a party for the orphanage. (151)
[we written above "us"]

19 Bob and *him* would like to play baseball with one of the major leagues someday. (149)
[he written above "him"]

20 When Dad came home from Atlantic City, he brought *we* girls some salt-water taffy. (155)
[us written above "we"]

38

Activity: How much can you learn about a word in a dictionary? Not only does the dictionary give every meaning of a word (some words have several meanings), but also it gives pronunciation, part of speech, derivation, standing as to usage (if below standard), syllabication, and often synonyms, antonyms, and other information of a general nature. Using your dictionary, list all the information you can find about the words **guerilla, meridian, symmetry, velocity,** and **villain.**

SCORE _____ (Top Score 20)

Pronoun Agreement

In each sentence write the correct pronoun for the antecedent given. Underline the antecedent of each pronoun that you write.

EXAMPLE: Students should take good care of ___*their*___ equipment.

1 Neither of the girls could find ___her___ skates.

2 Our debating team deserves ___its___ fine reputation.

3 Has each of the boys handed in ___his___ book report?

4 Each of the girls must furnish ___her___ own camping equipment.

5 Our band will wear ___their___ brand-new uniforms in the parade tomorrow.

6 Each of the classes should elect ___its___ officers by next week.

7 Each of the girls will have to make ___her___ own costume.

8 Each of the boys should be able to take care of ___himself___.

9 The committee will give ___its___ report at the next scheduled meeting.

10 The police have returned each of the cars to ___its___ rightful owner.

11 One of the boys has left ___his___ history notebook in the principal's office.

12 Not one of the girls had remembered to bring ___her___ money for dues.

13 Neither Jane nor Sally will enter ___her___ dog in the contest.

14 Either Bob or Dick should bring ___his___ car if it is possible.

15 Has any boy asked for a change in ___his___ schedule of classes?

16 Both Jim and Joan passed ___their___ English IV tests without any difficulty.

17 Each of the boys worked as hard as ___he___ could on plans for the masquerade party.

18 The students who are in the public-speaking class are doing ___their___ best work.

19 Neither girl would lend ___her___ assistance when we had a flat tire.

20 Neither of the boys assumes the responsibility that ___he___ should.

21 No boy should fail to hand in ___his___ report on the day that it is due.

22 Any one of the women here will give you ___her___ opinion on part-time jobs.

23 Every one of the boys should do ___his___ best to make our guests feel welcome.

24 Every girl on the hockey team realizes that ___she___ will have to work hard to win.

25 The girls on the winning team will receive ___their___ awards at the end of the meet.

Plain English Handbook, 129, 130, 142, 163–165.

Activity: Write the declension of the personal pronouns. *Plain English Handbook,* 144.

39

SCORE _____ (Top Score 50)

LESSON 30

Using Pronouns

In each sentence write the correct pronoun from within the parentheses.

EXAMPLE: The choice was between George and ____me____ (I/me).   (153)

1 All the guests are here but Marilyn and ____her____ (her/she).   (156)

2 Gary is coming to the party with Jane and ____me____ (I/me).   (153)

3 Jerry would not help Janet and ____me____ (I/me) fold the papers.   (272)

4 I believe that Kathryn is much younger than ____she____ (her/she).   (148)

5 Mother sent Margaret and ____me____ (me/I) a post card from Milan.   (154)

6 The coach is going with ____us____ (we/us) students to the picnic.   (157)

7 All ____we____ (we/us) acrobats have promised to perform at the carnival.   (151)

8 Was it ____they____ (they/them) who built the new house on the corner?   (152)

9 Sara repaired the typewriter for Jane and ____me____ (I/me).   (153)

10 Rod and ____they____ (they/them) are going to the circus next Saturday.   (149)

11 Was it ____she____ (she/her) who wrote the story that we liked so much?   (152)

12 Elena is the skier ____who____ (who/whom) we believe will win the race.   (160)

13 Is he the man ____whom____ (who/whom) you saw at the florist's yesterday?   (160)

14 Was it Gene and ____he____ (he/him) who were coming early to help us?   (152)

15 It must have been ____she____ (she/her) who left the book on the radiator.   (152)

16 Rafael and ____he____ (he/him) have promised to make all the arrangements.   (149)

17 Appoint ____whoever____ (whoever/whomever) has the most time to do the work.   (161)

18 The stranger helped Steve and ____him____ (he/him) put up the top of the old car.   (272)

19 Are you sure that Marge and ____he____ (he/him) will go to the beach with us?   (149)

20 Will you show ____us____ (we/us) girls the pictures that you took on your trip?   (155)

40

Activity: Since the greater part of communication is supplied by conversation, the ability to converse intelligently and correctly is just as important as the ability to write in proper forms. *Plain English Handbook,* 642, lists some of the finer points in the practice of conversation. Read this section and write a paragraph on one of the points listed, such as "Be a Good Listener."

SCORE _____ (Top Score 20)

LESSON 31

Reviewing Pronouns

Cross out each incorrect pronoun and write the correct form above it. If there is no incorrect pronoun, write **C** before the sentence.

                                 me

EXAMPLE: It might be she who will bring the election results to Tom and ~~I~~. (152, 153)

                                he

1 Robert and she are much taller than Joan and ~~him~~. (149, 148)

                    he

2 It must have been ~~him~~ who nominated Jean and her. (152, 159, 153)

                       who

3 Helen and she are candidates ~~whom~~ we think will make good officers. (149, 159)

      us

4 All of ~~we~~ photographers must take care of our own equipment. (157)

                      her

5 Either Eileen or Jane will bring ~~their~~ book for Fred and me. (163, 153)

                 me

6 Uncle Charles gave Jack and ~~I~~ the tickets for all of us boys. (154, 157)

C 7 Don and he have brought the stereo set upstairs for us girls. (149, 157)

                 her

8 Larry and I saw Paul and ~~she~~ bicycling in the park yesterday. (149, 153)

                         me

9 The principal and she divided the chores between George and ~~I~~. (149, 153)

       they

10 Helen and ~~them~~ will go to see the principal with Peggy and me. (149, 153)

                        her

11 All we sophomores have tickets to the ice show but Stan and ~~she~~. (151, 156)

                     her

12 Nan told Helen and me that every girl has handed in ~~their~~ report. (154, 164)

           he

13 Are you sure that it was ~~him~~ whom you saw get into the red cab? (152, 160)

       they

14 Sam and ~~them~~ will help Tom and him with the stage sets for the play. (149, 153)

                    us

15 Marge and I have asked Miss Wilson to go with ~~we~~ girls to an art exhibit. (149, 157)

   we

16 All ~~us~~ boys like our counselor. (151)

                      her

17 It couldn't have been they whom you saw with Jo and ~~she~~ last night. (152, 160, 153)

   he

18 Was it ~~him~~ who painted the picture that Hal and I saw in the window? (152, 160, 149)

           her

19 Every senior girl will do ~~their~~ best to help Ted and him with the new program. (164, 153)

               he

20 Every one of us boys knows that ~~they~~ should listen to the director and him. (157, 163, 153)

41

Activity: Writing a précis, or condensation, of an article, story, or paragraph is an excellent method to use in developing the ability to write well. Study sections 557–560 in *Plain English Handbook* and then select the material that you wish to condense. Try to reduce the number of words to one-third or one-fourth of the original, but be sure to retain all the meaning of the original.

SCORE _____ (Top Score 20)

Reviewing Nouns and Pronouns

Cross out each incorrect noun or pronoun and write the correct form above it.

　　　　　　　　　　　　　　　　me　　Hill
EXAMPLE:　Jack will meet Don and ~~I~~ at ~~Hill's~~ and Bird's Restaurant.　(153, 124)

　　　　　he　　she　　　　　　　　　　　women's
1　Was it ~~him~~ or ~~her~~ who hung up the men's and ~~womens'~~ coats?　(152, 122)

　　　who　　　　　　　　　　　　　　I
2　Is it she ~~whom~~ you say is more patient than ~~me~~?　(152, 159, 148)

　　　　　　　　　he whom
3　Are you sure it was ~~him who~~ you saw with us boys?　(152, 160, 157)

　Who　　　　　　　　　us
4　~~Whom~~ did you say would take ~~we~~ hockey players out to the skating rink?　(159, 155)

　　we　　　　　　　　　her
5　All ~~us~~ juniors but Sara and ~~she~~ have already ordered our yearbooks.　(151, 156)

　Whomever
6　~~Whoever~~ you appoint will work on the committee with Anne and me.　(162, 153)

　　　　　　I　　　　　　　　　　　　sister-in-law's
7　Corina and ~~me~~ are going to have lunch on my ~~sister's-in-law~~ patio.　(149, 123)

　　　　he whom　　　　　　　　　　　　　　me
8　It is ~~him who~~ you should send to the library with Hal and ~~I~~.　(152, 159, 153)

　　　　　　　　they　　　　　　　　　　　her
9　It must have been ~~them~~ whom you saw talking with John and ~~she~~.　(152, 160, 153)

　　　　　　he　　　　　　　boys'
10　It was not ~~him~~ who took the two ~~boy's~~ car without telling them.　(152, 160, 121)

　　　　she who
11　Is it ~~her whom~~ you think deserves the scholarship to the university?　(152, 160)

　　　　　I　　　bucketfuls
12　Ed and ~~me~~ carried ~~bucketsful~~ of water to the pickers working in the fields.　(149, 87)

　　　　　　　　　whoever　　　　　　　us
13　Take the tickets to ~~whomever~~ has volunteered to sell them for ~~we~~ girls.　(161, 157)

　　　　　Ruth's　　　　　　　her
14　Have you heard of ~~Ruth~~ visiting Peg and ~~she~~ at a resort in Pennsylvania?　(127, 153)

　　　　　　　she　　　　　　　　　　　　us
15　It might have been ~~her~~ who arranged the swimming party for ~~we~~ girls.　(152, 159, 157)

　　children's　　　　　　　　　　me
16　The ~~childrens'~~ mother came to see Leah and ~~I~~ about baby-sitting with them.　(122, 153)

　　　　　he
17　Was it ~~him~~ whom you wanted to go out to get sandwiches for us girls?　(152, 160, 157)

　　　　　　　　her　　　　　　　　　　its
18　Each girl will do ~~their~~ best to help the club retain ~~their~~ tennis trophy.　(164, 165)

　　　I　　　　　　　　　　　　　brothers-in-law
19　Al and ~~me~~ saw many elk when we visited his ~~brother-in-laws~~ in Wyoming.　(149, 89, 86)

　　　　　　　　　　his　　　　whoever
20　Every boy should cast ~~their~~ vote for ~~whomever~~ will make the best chairperson.　(164, 160)

Activity: When you are speaking on the telephone, the person to whom you are speaking has nothing to judge you by except your voice. Is yours a polite and pleasant telephone manner? Dramatize several different telephone calls with your classmates. You might call a friend who has been sick, make an airplane reservation, make an appointment with a doctor, or invite someone to a party. Have a period of criticism at the conclusion of each dramatization. *Plain English Handbook,* 644.

SCORE ＿＿＿＿＿＿ (Top Score 40)

LESSON 33

Using Adjectives and Adverbs/1

To complete each sentence, select the better form of the adjective or the adverb from within the parentheses.

EXAMPLE: The tea tasted so ___sweet___ (sweet/sweetly) that I did not drink it. (289)

1 What ___kind of___ (kind of/kind of a) sports car was he driving? (307)

2 John is not ___so___ (so/as) eager to go to college as Billy. (310)

3 Gina plays tennis ___well___ (well/good) for a beginner. (329)

4 On the golf course you can beat me ___easily___ (easy/easily). (339)

5 We couldn't find ___any___ (no/any) pictures that we liked. (336)

6 Ed is taller than ___any other___ (any/any other) person in our class. (298)

7 Jo likes any of ___these___ (this/these) kinds of books, I am sure. (302)

8 This new recipe is not much different ___from___ (from/than) that old one. (337)

9 We ___surely___ (sure/surely) had a good time at your luncheon party. (311)

10 I feel ___different___ (different/differently) about the book now. (289, 312)

11 We were ___almost___ (most/almost) home when the storm broke. (328)

12 Of the two cities, isn't Salem the ___larger___ (larger/largest)? (296)

13 Martha seems ___rather___ (rather/sort of) unhappy today. (333)

14 Do you like ___that___ (those/that) kind of magazine? (302)

15 Mr. Kane let us omit the ___last five___ (five last/last five) questions. (303)

16 I made ___fewer___ (less/fewer) errors on my test this time. (306)

17 I walked aimlessly, going ___nowhere___ (nowhere/nowheres) in particular. (330)

18 Who is to take ___an___ (a/an) aptitude test today? (286)

19 Jody feels ___somewhat___ (some/somewhat) better this evening. (334)

20 I think it is the ___better___ (best/better) of the two programs. (296)

43

Activity: Draw an arrow from each adjective or adverb you selected to the word it modifies.

Spelling List/5

advantages	preliminary	plateau	cozy	illustrate
welfare	conversation	ceremony	appearance	suspense
scientist	incidentally	social	earnest	requirements
future	mirror	miniature	recognition	impression
prairie	enormous	eventually	cashier	recognize
television	certificate	grandeur	glorious	definite
previously	declaration	rescued	musician	delinquents
foliage	volunteered	preferred	character	tomorrow

SCORE _____ (Top Score 20)

Using Adjectives and Adverbs/2

Make all necessary corrections in the use of adjectives and adverbs in the manner indicated in the example.

That   *surely*   *other*
EXAMPLE: ~~That there~~ boy ~~sure~~ has less ambition than any‸applicant in the room. (674, 311, 298)

           rather
1 Most of the youngsters feel ~~kind of~~ bad about missing the game. (333)
         really (*or* very)
2 She surely does write ~~real~~ well for one with so little training. (311)
                        bitter
3 The warmed-over coffee smelled good, but it tasted ~~bitterly.~~ (289, 312)
                      ten-day
4 Mr. Kemp is planning to go to California for a ~~ten-days~~ vacation. (299)
                                from
5 I thought our new shoes were alike, but yours are different ~~than~~ mine. (337)
   so   heavier
6 Hal is not ~~as~~ tall as Bob, but he is the ~~heaviest~~ of the two. (310, 296)
       well   carefully
7 Although the car ran ~~good,~~ we drove down the highway very ~~careful.~~ (329, 311)
           so
8 There were not ~~as~~ many students taking German last year as this year. (310)
     surely   suddenly
9 We were ~~sure~~ surprised that the leaves had changed color so ~~sudden.~~ (311)
                           other
10 I polished Dad's car, and now it is shinier than any‸car on our street. (298)
     bad   somewhat
11 Helen feels ~~badly~~ because she is ~~kind of~~ behind in her studying. (289, 312, 333)
                      really (*or* very)
12 I have heard that the last three stories in this new book are ~~real~~ good. (303, 311)
        almost   well
13 Margaret speaks French ~~most as good as~~ a Parisian would speak. (328, 329)
     somewhat   from
14 This movie is ~~some~~ different ~~than~~ the book from which it was adapted. (334, 337)
      beautiful   differently
15 The room looks ~~beautifully~~ with the furniture arranged ~~different.~~ (289, 312, 311)
   very (*or* really)   fewer
16 We are ~~real~~ glad that there are ~~less~~ car accidents happening every week. (311, 306)
     differently
17 If he had talked ~~different,~~ he would have made more friends while he was here. (311)
      sweet   sweeter
18 Both perfumes smell ~~sweetly,~~ but this is the ~~sweetest~~ of the two. (289, 312, 296)
                    well
19 Don't you think the governor talked ~~good~~ on the television program last night? (329)
                      better
20 I have read two new books, and I think *The Great Bridge* is the ~~best.~~ (296)
           better
21 He is not so tall as Ted, but he is the ~~best~~ basketball player of the two. (310, 296)
   was never able (*or omit* never)
22 Ed ~~wasn't never able~~ to get from gym to Spanish class by the time the bell rang. (336)
                     an
23 A Swiss boy, a Korean girl, and ~~a~~ Italian boy are exchange students in our class. (286)
                   fewer   this
24 Due to our safety engineers, there are ~~less~~ accidents of ~~these~~ kind every day. (306, 302)
                 eloquently
25 The attorney seemed sincere, and she spoke ~~eloquent~~ about the innocence of the man. (311)

Activity: Draw an arrow from each adjective or adverb you corrected to the word it modifies.

44

Using Prepositions and Conjunctions

Cross out each incorrect preposition or conjunction and write the correct form above it.

with

EXAMPLE: Robert and I differ ~~from~~ one another about music.   (360)

1 Is Will still angry ~~with~~ *at* the television set?   (351)

2 Did that book say that John Keats died ~~from~~ *of* tuberculosis?   (358)

3 The generous stranger seemed eager to part ~~from~~ *with* his money.   (362)

4 The wind has blown your letter ~~in back of~~ *behind* the desk.   (363)

5 John was getting ~~off of~~ *off* the airplane when we saw him.   (364)

6 I liked the movie, but it was quite different ~~than~~ *from* the book.   (361)

7 We had hardly started on our trip ~~than~~ *when* the accident occurred.   (384)

8 Mr. Potter will probably return from his vacation ~~inside of~~ *within* a week.   (356)

9 The old man was angry ~~at~~ *with* the boys who were teasing the dogs in the park.   (351)

10 Aunt Sarah still comes to see us on Sunday just ~~like~~ *as* she always has done.   (372)

11 He is sure to fail his history exam ~~except~~ *unless* he spends more time studying.   (370)

12 Barbara isn't sure ~~if~~ *whether* she is going to Stanford University or to Columbia.   (381)

13 Although the twins look alike, they differ ~~with~~ *from* each other in disposition.   (360)

14 Karen is practicing her swimming strokes exactly ~~like~~ *as* the coach told her.   (372)

15 I never see your old house ~~without I wish~~ *that I do not wish* that you were still living there.   (371)

16 As we watched, the man jumped ~~in~~ *into* the river from the bridge to save the boy.   (357)

17 I do not feel ~~as~~ *that* we should be taking this road because it looks very rough.   (379)

18 Only one other person ~~beside~~ *besides* Jim knows of the surprise that we are planning.   (353)

19 I think the responsibilities should be divided evenly ~~between~~ *among* the four girls.   (354)

20 The seniors differ ~~from~~ *with* the juniors about a gift to the school.   (360)

21 During the storm last night, heavy rains fell ~~among~~ *between* Atlanta, Macon, and Savannah.   (355)

22 It was an unhappy day for Jim Keath, hero of *Moccasin Trail*, when he parted ~~with~~ *from* the Crow Indians.   (362)

23 At the age of seventeen, Benjamin Franklin arrived ~~at~~ *in* Philadelphia with one silver dollar in his pocket.   (352)

24 Although she could neither see ~~or~~ *nor* hear, Helen Keller was graduated from Radcliffe College with honors.   (378)

25 I saw on television ~~where~~ *that* the governor has called a special session of the state legislature.   (380)

45

SCORE _____ (Top Score 25)

Reviewing Modifiers and Connectives

Cross out each incorrect adjective, adverb, preposition, or conjunction and write the correct form above it. If there is no incorrect word, write **C** before the sentence.

bad
EXAMPLE: Nan felt ~~badly~~ about the accident that she had caused.   (289, 312)

1 There are ~~less~~ *fewer* seniors than juniors in our debating club this year.   (330)

2 People who are going ~~nowheres~~ *nowhere* always seem to be in a hurry.   (312)

3 Bob is ~~some~~ *somewhat* better today, but he still feels weak.   (334, 289, 312)

4 Tom does his work carefully, just ~~like~~ *as* his older sister did.   (372)

C 5 This shirt is different from the one I bought last week.   (337, 361)

6 Francesca said that there wasn't ~~no one~~ *anyone (or* was no one*)* at the station to meet her.   (336)

7 Craig doesn't know ~~if~~ *whether* the new museum is opening tomorrow or next Saturday.   (381)

8 The larger of the two beagle puppies has jumped ~~off of~~ *off* the chair.   (296, 364)

9 Few people feel ~~good~~ *well* when they get too much sun.   (289, 312)

10 Which do you think is the ~~best~~ *better* of these two pictures of Joan?   (296, 302)

11 The coach feels ~~badly~~ *bad* whenever our teams do not play well.   (289, 312, 329)

12 If we divide the job ~~between~~ *among* the four of us, we should get it done quickly.   (354)

13 Ellen would not go to bed ~~except~~ *unless* I agreed to read "Goldilocks" to her.   (370)

C14 Ann and I always differ with one another on modern art.   (360)

15 She paints unusually ~~good,~~ *well* but she has no interest in becoming an artist.   (329)

16 Fred ran swiftly to the edge of the ocean and plunged ~~in~~ *into* the waves.   (311, 357)

17 You surely read in the paper ~~where~~ *that* we are going to have a new school.   (311, 380)

18 We think that Joan plays ball ~~most as~~ *almost* well as her brother did last year.   (328, 329)

19 Surely Hal and he will finish the research and the report ~~inside of~~ *within* a week.   (311, 356)

20 The older of the two boys looked ~~doubtfully~~ *doubtful* when I said they could go.   (296, 312)

Activity: Figures of speech are used in writing and in speaking to obtain a desired effect. The six main figures of speech are *simile, metaphor, personification, hyperbole, metonymy,* and *synecdoche.* Study Section 676–682 in *Plain English Handbook* and then write six sentences, using one of the figures of speech in each sentence. Find good examples of figures of speech in poetry and prose, and discuss them in class.

SCORE _____ (Top Score 20)

Reviewing Verbs, Nouns, and Pronouns

Cross out each incorrect verb, noun, or pronoun and write the correct form above it.

EXAMPLE: Was it ~~her~~ *she* who practiced with Kay and him? (152)

1 Ted and I went to the play rehearsal and ~~set~~ *sat* near the front of the room. (149, 204, 217)

2 Neither Nora nor she knows whether you ~~was~~ *were* given the leading role. (237, 260)

3 After we performers had rehearsed our dance, we ~~laid~~ *lay* on some benches to rest. (151, 204, 217)

4 The principal and the play's director think that a hundred dollars ~~are~~ *is* too much to pay for renting costumes. (245)

5 Ms. Young is going to look at some of the costume designs that Bob and ~~I drawed~~ *drew*. (149, 204)

6 Our director is one of those teachers who ~~is~~ *are* always ready to help us students. (241, 147)

7 Mr. Lamas, not the students, ~~have~~ *has* asked Ed and him to get sandwiches. (261, 272)

8 If I ~~was~~ *were* she, I'd ask Carita and him to paint scenery for the play. (256, 272)

9 Lou should send the program design to ~~he~~ *him*, the chairperson of the program committee. (157)

10 Mrs. Marsh, as well as some teachers, ~~were~~ *was* at rehearsal when Gail and I arrived. (236, 149)

11 Ms. Young and he are actors ~~whom~~ *who* we think will do all they can for us amateurs. (149, 159, 157)

12 All we girls but Liz and ~~she~~ *her* were very pleased with our costumes. (151, 156)

13 I helped Joe and him unpack and sort out three ~~cartonsful~~ *cartonfuls* of stage props. (272, 87)

14 Neither Miss Yee-Ren nor the girls ~~was~~ *were* here when Bill and I came. (238, 149, 204)

15 Grace and she took the ~~childrens'~~ *children's* parts until the two children arrived. (149, 122)

16 Could it have been ~~them~~ *they* whom Joe and he saw backstage earlier today? (152, 160, 149, 204)

17 Here ~~comes~~ *come* Mr. Blake and the stage crew to set up for us performers. (239, 157)

18 Every one of the stagehands ~~are~~ *is* here to help Chuck and me with the scenery. (246, 153)

19 Tom ~~don't~~ *doesn't* know for sure that it was they whom he saw in the audience. (197, 152, 160, 204)

20 I am sure all we others of the cast are sadder than ~~her~~ *she* that the play is over. (151, 148)

47

SCORE _____ (Top Score 20)

Reviewing Verb and Pronoun Agreement

Cross out each incorrect verb or pronoun and write the correct form above it.

EXAMPLE: The students, not the teacher, ~~was~~ *were* in charge of the program. (261)

1 Jane and ~~her~~ *she* think it is ~~me.~~ *I* (149, 152)

2 Bacon and eggs ~~are~~ *is* the only dish that Amanda can prepare. (247)

3 Each of the boys ~~play~~ *plays* as if he alone ~~was~~ *were* responsible for winning the game. (242, 258)

4 Jack and ~~me~~ *I* think that each of the groups should elect ~~their~~ *its* own officers. (149, 163)

5 All ~~us~~ *we* spectators are proud that our team has won its last six games. (151, 165)

6 Neither the girls nor John ~~were~~ *was* interested in going to the fair with us. (238)

7 Here ~~comes~~ *come* Jay and the boys to go to the bus stop with Susan and ~~I.~~ *me* (239, 153)

8 Tod and he have gone, and there ~~goes~~ *go* Miss Webb and the others now. (149, 239)

9 A number of ~~we~~ *us* boys ~~was~~ *were* at the gym when the other team arrived. (157, 244)

10 Hal and he think that she is the trainer ~~who~~ *whom* they met at the rodeo yesterday. (149, 160)

11 Every girl knows that ~~they~~ *she* must help the team maintain its good record. (164, 165)

12 It was ~~her~~ *she* who announced that each boy should bring ~~their~~ *his* own lunch. (152, 142)

13 Either Paul or she ~~have~~ *has* gone to help Ellie and ~~she~~ *her* bring the phonograph. (237, 153)

14 ~~Us~~ *We* friends know that Gail is one of those people who ~~is~~ *are* always complaining. (151, 241)

15 Neither he nor his parents think that ten miles ~~are~~ *is* too far to go to a ball game. (238, 245)

16 Peggy, as well as her brothers, ~~were~~ *was* glad when her mother ~~come~~ *came* home. (236, 204)

Activity: Write five sentences in which you use the relative pronouns **who, whose, whom, whoever,** and **whomever.** Write the use of each relative pronoun above it in each sentence that you write.

Spelling List/6

tough	graduation	preference	strength	applause
Christian	undoubtedly	communicate	arrangement	antique
sanitary	ancestors	familiar	naturally	worry
wondered	stretched	friendship	desperate	universe
missionary	practically	profession	already	ascend
vaccine	eccentric	sociable	varied	moisture
gymnasium	inaugurated	hazards	annoyance	throughout
commission	appreciate	areas	splendid	applicants

SCORE _____ (Top Score 25)

LESSON 39

Reviewing Verbs and Pronouns

To complete each of the following sentences, select a verb or pronoun from the group at the right of each sentence that is lettered the same as the blank.

EXAMPLE: Neither Don nor the girls a___*were*___ on the raft

ªwere/was

when Joe and b___*I*___ swam out. (238, 149)

bI/me

1 Was it a___she___ b___who___ came out to the farm with

1 ªher/she bwho/whom

Marian and c___him___? (152, 160, 153)

che/him

2 If I a___had___ saved my money, I could have b___gone___

2 ªhad/have

to Boston with Terry. (368, 204)

bgone/went

3 All a___we___ candidates have b___done___ some cam-

3 ªwe/us bdid/done

paigning except Gary and c___him___. (151, 216, 153)

che/him

4 Joe and a___I___ think that every girl on the crew will do

4 ªI/me

b___her___ part. (149, 164)

btheir/her

5 There a___were___ three of b___us___ counselors who

5 ªwas/were bwe/us

c___came___ to camp early. (239, 157, 216)

ccame/come

6 Do you think it was a___they___ who said that neither Dick

6 ªthey/them

nor he b___was___ elected? (152, 237)

bwas/were

7 a___Were___ you there when the coach, as well as the players,

7 ªWas/Were

b___was___ applauded loudly? (260, 236)

bwas/were

8 It is a___he___ who b___is___ to arrange the top shelf

8 ªhim/he bis/am

because he is taller than c___she___. (152, 249, 148)

cshe/her

9 We haven't a___seen___ Lynn since the window was

9 ªseen/saw

b___broken___ when she tried to c___raise___ it. (204)

bbroke/broken craise/rise

10 Tim and a___she___ have already gone home, but one of the

10 ªshe/her

announcers b___is___ still here. (149, 246)

bis/are

49

SCORE _____ (Top Score 25)

LESSON 40

Reviewing General Usage

Cross out each incorrectly used word and write the correct form above it. If there is no incorrect word, write C before the sentence.

EXAMPLE: Tod and I think that we will leave for home ~~inside of~~ *within* a week. (356)

1 Does the coach object to ~~us~~ our going with Frank and him? (270, 153)

2 You shouldn't feel bad because you do not sing ~~good~~ well. (289, 329)

3 ~~Is~~ Are Jerry and Beth going in the boat with Paul and me? (247, 153)

4 Tom, Jackie, and I will go in his ~~father's-in-law~~ father-in-law's boat. (149, 123)

5 All ~~us~~ we boys have our bus tickets except Joe and ~~he~~ him. (151, 153)

6 Ramona and he work in the ~~mens'~~ men's department of the same store. (149, 122)

7 Frank and he cannot hope to succeed ~~except~~ unless they do good work. (149, 370)

8 We organizers should have set this chair ~~in back of~~ behind the desk. (151, 217, 363)

9 If some of us students would study ~~different~~ differently, we might have better grades. (157, 311, 293)

10 This is the ~~largest~~ larger of the two melons, but it tastes bitter. (296, 289)

11 Our principal is ~~sure~~ surely pleased that there are ~~less~~ fewer students failing. (311, 306)

50 12 Is it he ~~whom~~ who you think works harder than Bill or ~~me~~ I? (152, 160, 148)

C 13 It might have been he whom you saw with Dorita and her. (152, 160, 153)

14 Are you sure it was Bob and he who brought the letters to Bess and ~~I~~ me? (152, 160, 153)

15 All we students were pleased that our team wore ~~its~~ their new uniforms. (151, 165)

16 Could it have been ~~her~~ she whom Hal and ~~me~~ I saw with Kit and him? (152, 160, 149, 153)

17 The coach does not know yet ~~whom~~ who will go in the car with Ann and me. (160, 153)

C 18 Every one of us students was proud of Tom's winning the trophy. (246, 157, 270)

19 If I ~~was~~ were she, I'd ask Lucilla and ~~he~~ him to help with the planning. (256, 153)

20 She is one of those persons who ~~is~~ are always eager to help us students. (241, 157)

Activity: Write a letter of thanks to someone who has entertained you at a party or who has sent you a gift. You may have to invent a situation, but make it sound real. *Plain English Handbook,* 617 and 619.

SCORE _____ (Top Score 25)

LESSON 41

Reviewing Troublesome Usages

Cross out each incorrectly used word and write the correct form above it. If there is no incorrect word, write **C** before the sentence.

                      she   *they*   *are*

EXAMPLE: Jack and ~~her~~ said it is ~~them~~ who ~~is~~ to drive. (149, 152, 249)

                            is   better

1 How do you know that their team ~~are~~ the ~~best~~ of the two? (240, 296)

                                lie

2 Mother, if you are really tired, ~~lay~~ down for a while. (204, 217)

                          makes

3 Her friendliness, not her talents, ~~make~~ everyone like her. (261)

                            from

4 The first report was that he had died ~~of~~ exposure. (358)

C 5 The athlete strained to raise herself higher on the bar. (204, 217)

                  so

6 Georgia is not ~~as~~ likely to give in as John. (310)

                    his

7 Each boy must bring ~~their~~ own equipment for the camping trip. (164)

                      sitting

8 Those boys have been ~~setting~~ by the pool all afternoon. (204, 217)

                teach

9 Jim wants to ~~learn~~ me to play the drums. (227)

             have

10 We should ~~of~~ gone home after the last inning. (230)

            brothers-in-law

11 My two ~~brother-in-laws~~ are going to help me build a boat. (86)

    Within

12 ~~Inside of~~ a month I will be able to buy more records. (356)

                  whether

13 She doesn't know yet ~~if~~ she will be able to go to Chicago with us. (381)

               was   me

14 Each of the athletes ~~were~~ eager to go with the coach and ~~I~~. (242, 153)

We   are

15 ~~Us~~ reporters find him to be one of those people who ~~is~~ very uncooperative. (151, 272, 241)

       he   her

16 There go ~~him~~ and Shirley with Don and ~~she~~. (239, 153)

    children's

17 The ~~childrens'~~ parents are planning a party for the holidays. (122)

               those

18 No one wants to help ~~them~~ boys clean the garage. (168)

           well

19 Linda reads ~~good~~ for a child of her age. (329)

us   Sue's

20 All of ~~we~~ sophomores were proud of ~~Sue~~ winning the tennis match. (157, 270)

Activity: In formal writing, there are types of expressions which should usually be avoided. These inappropriate types are labeled **archaic, barbarisms, colloquialisms, improprieties, neologisms, provincialisms, slang, vulgarisms, hackneyed** (or **trite**) **expressions,** and **idiomatic expressions.** Study sections 654–664 in *Plain English Handbook* and make a list of several of each type.

SCORE _____ (Top Score 25)

LESSON 42

Review of Reviews

Cross out each incorrectly used word and write the correct form above it. If there is no incorrect word, write C before the sentence.

EXAMPLE: We could ~~of~~ *have* finished this job today if we had begun yesterday. (230, 204)

1 There ~~goes~~ *go* Henry and Herb outside to raise the flag. (239, 217)

2 If I were ~~her,~~ *she* I'd use only two ~~capsful~~ *capfuls* of paint thinner. (152, 87)

3 ~~Is~~ *Are* Kate and Margot to help Ted and him with the program? (247, 153)

4 Mary and he danced ~~good~~ *well* as a team and they looked wonderful. (149, 329, 289)

5 One of the skaters in the chorus of the ice show ~~are~~ *is* staying with my cousin. (246)

6 There wasn't ~~no one~~ *anyone (or was no one)* else with John and ~~I~~ *me* when we saw the accident. (336, 153, 204)

7 That girl who came with Ed and me is the ~~oldest~~ *older* of the two sisters. (160, 153, 296)

8 Although the boys played well, they feel ~~badly~~ *bad* because they were defeated. (329, 289)

9 Miss Grayson, not the girls, ~~have~~ *has* asked Dan and me to help. (261, 272)

C 10 It was he who said that each of the girls brings her lunch. (152, 160, 163)

11 Could it have been ~~them~~ *they* who were with Buck and her at the horse show? (152, 153)

12 Pat and he behaved so ~~bad~~ *badly* that Tom will not baby-sit with them again. (149, 311)

13 There ~~was~~ *were* sixteen people in the chorus and they all sang ~~beautiful.~~ *beautifully* (239, 311)

14 ~~Us~~ *We* students are surely making ~~less~~ *fewer* errors in our grammar now. (151, 311, 306)

15 All of us girls know that our club has cause to be proud of ~~their~~ *its* record. (157, 165)

C 16 Judy and I had done our work and had gone home when Nan came. (149, 204)

17 Neither Sal nor Lou ~~were~~ *was* at Stone and King's Store when I got there. (237, 124)

18 Tom and ~~her~~ *she* say it is ~~them~~ *they* who are to go in their car with them. (149, 152)

19 It was they who hung up the men's and ~~womens'~~ *women's* coats at the party. (152, 122)

20 When we came, Antonio and he had gone ~~somewheres.~~ *somewhere* (330)

52

Activity: Write a letter of application for a part-time job that you have heard or read about. Remember that a letter of application is your first introduction to a possible employer and you want to make a good impression. *Plain English Handbook,* 590–603, 605.

Sentence Structure

This test parallels, in content, Inventory 4, page 109.

I. *Sentence Parts*

(Lessons 43–45)   20 Points

Indicate whether the italicized group of words in each sentence is a phrase or a clause by writing **P** or **C** before the sentence. On the line provided, rewrite the sentence, changing each phrase to a clause and each clause to a phrase. (Correct answers may vary.)

EXAMPLE· <u>P</u> The girl *swimming in the pool* is Jean.

The girl who is swimming in the pool is Jean.

<u>C</u> 1 *When the sound of the wind died,* silence was everywhere.
The sound of the wind having died, silence was everywhere.

<u>C</u> 2 The woman *who is chopping wood* is Mrs. Chris.
The woman chopping wood is Mrs. Chris.

<u>P</u> 3 *Realizing the humor of the situation,* Marty laughed with the rest of us.
When he realized the humor of the situation, Marty laughed with the rest of us.

<u>C</u> 4 *When we visited Vermont last March,* we learned about maple sugaring.
Visiting Vermont last March, we learned about maple sugaring.

<u>P</u> 5 *Thinking of the exciting day to come,* Suzie found it difficult to sleep.
Suzie, who was thinking about the exciting day to come, found it difficult to sleep.

<u>P</u> 6 The snow *blowing around the buildings* looked ghostly.
The snow, which was blowing around the buildings, looked ghostly.

<u>P</u> 7 *Driving into the garage,* Tom saw Ed's car.
As he drove into the garage, Tom saw Ed's car.

<u>P</u> 8 *Anticipating a rain storm,* we took our umbrellas.
Since we anticipated a rain storm, we took our umbrellas.

<u>C</u> 9 *Although Jo knew the job was temporary,* she accepted it.
Knowing the job to be temporary, Jo accepted it.

<u>C</u> 10 *Because Lee arrived early,* she helped Mrs. Field.
Arriving early, Lee helped Mrs. Field.

II. *Sentence Effectiveness*

(Lessons 46–50)   10 Points

Each item consists of two expressions of the same thought. Draw a ring around **A** or **B** to indicate which is the better sentence.

EXAMPLE·   **A** Arranged on a corner shelf, Janet found the antique cups.
(B) Janet found the antique cups arranged on a corner shelf.

1 **A** Pam is Mark's sister, and she is spending the summer in San Francisco.
(B) Pam, Mark's sister, is spending the summer in San Francisco.

2 **A** Nancy saw a pants suit and a sweater in a shop window which she liked.

  (**B**) In a shop window Nancy saw a pants suit and a sweater which she liked.

3 **A** Standing on the hill, the autumn sunset was brilliant.

  (**B**) Standing on the hill, we saw the brilliant autumn sunset.

4 (**A**) Walking quickly, we reached home before the rain started.

  B Walking quickly, home was reached before the rain started.

5 **A** Sue told Kay that she had been elected president.

  (**B**) Sue said, "Kay, you have been elected president."

6 (**A**) Stan likes to read poetry, especially poems by Robert Frost.

  B Stan likes to read poetry. Especially poems by Robert Frost.

7 (**A**) When traveling in Italy, we enjoyed skiing in the Italian Alps.

  B When traveling in Italy, skiing in the Italian Alps was enjoyed.

8 **A** All the students had a good time. When they celebrated the victory.

  (**B**) All the students had a good time when they celebrated the victory.

9 (**A**) Sam is busy studying because he is going to take the college entrance examination.

  B Sam is busy studying. Because he is going to take the college entrance examination.

10 (**A**) The sophomores are working hard, decorating the gym for the dance.

  B The sophomores are working hard. Decorating the gym for the dance.

III. *Words in the Sentence*

  (Lessons 51–54)   20 Points

Cross out each incorrectly used word and write the correct form above it.

                come

EXAMPLE: Here ~~comes~~ the boys walking down the beach with Joanie and her.

                    they

1 All of my teammates thinks it is ~~them~~ who are to blame for losing the game.

     were   *us*

2 There ~~was~~ some of ~~we~~ girls who did not think you were responsible for losing it.

                          rose

3 As I came into the room, the famous world traveler ~~raised~~ to her feet and spoke.

          *should (*or omit* had)*   *her*

4 Some one else ~~had ought to~~ help Kay and ~~she~~ carry the lunch down to the beach.

    she   *within*

5 Louise and ~~her~~ should be back from Mexico City ~~inside of~~ a week, I believe.

         from

6 This book is different ~~than~~ the other, but I think that it is the better of the two.

  were   *any (*or* is no)*

7 If I ~~was~~ he, I would go fishing, and there isn't ~~no~~ reason for his not going.

    have   *whom*

8 Could it ~~of~~ been she ~~who~~ we saw in the restaurant with Janet and him?

           teach

9 The coach and I are trying to ~~learn~~ Bill and him a new play.

          was

10 Neither Bob nor Celia ~~were~~ at home when Hank and he went to see them last night.

                        well

11 Juliana is younger than she, and she surely does talk ~~good~~ for a two-year-old.

                   pitcherfuls

12 It was they who helped us drink nearly three ~~pitchersful~~ of lemonade at lunch.

            who

13 Jake and he are the boys ~~whom~~ we think will help Jill and me at the rummage sale.

          were

14 Neither the dog nor the cats ~~was~~ at the door to greet me when I came home.

             fewer

15 Alice is much younger than he, but she makes ~~less~~ mistakes in French.

54

SCORE _____ (Top Score 50)

Phrases and Clauses

The italicized group of words in each sentence is either a phrase or a clause. On the lines provided, rewrite each sentence, changing each italicized phrase to a clause and each italicized clause to a phrase. (Correct answers may vary.)

EXAMPLE: *When we toured the museum,* we saw many art treasures.

Touring the museum, we saw many art treasures.

1 Joe has often told us *of his longing to travel through Asia.*
   Joe has often told us that he longs to travel through Asia.

2 *Waiting for the others to come,* Elaine and I played table tennis.
   While we waited for the others to come, Elaine and I played table tennis.

3 *As they walked along Fifth Avenue,* they looked in all the windows.
   Walking along Fifth Avenue, they looked in all the windows.

4 The player *who is at bat now* is Tony Perez.
   The player at bat now is Tony Perez.

5 *The girls just coming to camp* are eager to see the new pool.
   The girls who are just coming to camp are eager to see the new pool.

6 The old cottage *that overlooks the ocean* is falling apart.
   The old cottage overlooking the ocean is falling apart.

7 *As I watched television intently,* I let my plate drop to the floor.
   Watching television intently, I let my plate drop to the floor.

8 The author, *encouraged by the literary critics' praise,* started another novel.
   The author, who was encouraged by the critics' praise, started another novel.

9 *After I washed the car,* I applied a coat of wax.
   After washing the car, I applied a coat of wax.

Plain English Handbook, 387–409, 422.

55

Spelling List/7

ambitious	boulevard	reservoirs	convince	daughter
superstition	delicious	interpret	assure	represents
afterwards	assortment	curious	frightened	bureau
revolution	scholars	primitive	research	cellar
possibility	phrase	caution	officials	financially
audience	continuous	reciprocate	fought	registration
valid	merchants	circular	reputation	exactly
immense	compelled	fortunate	obliged	recipes

SCORE _____ (Top Score 9)

LESSON 44

Variety in Sentence Beginnings

On the first line classify the italicized beginning of each sentence by writing one of these symbols:

v for verb
adv for adverb

adj for adjective
d c for dependent clause
obj v for object of verb

part for participial phrase
prep for prepositional phrase

On the second line classify each sentence as to form by writing **S** for simple, **Cd** for compound, **Cx** for complex, or **Cd-Cx** for compound-complex.

EXAMPLE: __*adv*__ __S__ *Silently* the little boy slipped into the room.

d c	Cx	1 *While Dan and I were in England,* we had many interesting experiences.
adv	S	2 *Most* interesting perhaps was our tour of the Lake District.
part	S	3 *Wearing a fisherman's knit sweater and carrying a walking stick,* Dan looked like a British walker.
part	S	4 *Armed with a good map, a compass, and plenty of sandwiches,* we walked all day.
adj	S	5 *Treeless,* fog-covered mountains made the scenery solemnly beautiful.
v	S	6 *Have* you ever been to the Rocky Mountains?
adv	Cx	7 *Much* smaller in scale than the Rockies, these British mountains are nevertheless beautiful, scenic, and rugged.
adj	S	8 *Narrow* footpaths took us over hills and into villages.
adv	Cd	9 *Boldly* we made some strenuous climbs; we saw wonderful waterfalls and lakes.
part	Cx	10 *Having walked twenty-five miles in a day,* we felt we enjoyed our rest in a youth hostel.
prep	S	11 *Throughout our trip,* the weather was perfect.
d c	Cd-Cx	12 *Since we were both used to city living,* it was strange to walk from one village to the next; we had a new perspective on the countryside.
prep	S	13 *During our walk,* we'd meet and talk with other hikers.
adv	S	14 *Very* often, small animals like stoats crossed our path.
adv	Cx	15 *Sometimes* farm dogs would bark at us as we crossed farm fields.
part	S	16 *Sitting on top of a mountain,* we felt strangely moved.
v	Cd	17 *Reach* up, and you can almost touch the sky.
obj v	S	18 *Memories* of this we will always have.
adv	S	19 *Also* enjoyable were our visits at the hostels.
d c	Cx	20 *As we looked back,* we thought of the interesting people from many countries we had met.

56

Plain English Handbook, 410–416, 422, 425–431.

SCORE _____ (Top Score 40)

Variety in Sentence Structure

On the first line classify the italicized group of words in each sentence. If the group of words is a clause, write **C**. If the group of words is a phrase, indicate the kind of phrase by writing **prep** if it is a prepositional phrase, **abs** if it is an absolute construction, **app** if it is an appositive, or **part** if it is a participial phrase.

On the second line classify each sentence according to its structure, or form, by writing **S** for simple, **Cd** for compound, **Cx** for complex, or **Cd-Cx** for compound-complex.

		abs	S
EXAMPLE:	*The painting finished,* we drove out to the lake.		
1	Betty Morris, *who is my cousin,* is president of our class.	C	Cx
2	*The president being absent,* we did not have a meeting today.	abs	S
3	Betty Morris, *the president of our class,* is my cousin; but I did not vote for her.	app	Cd
4	The girl *who is president* is Betty Morris; she is my cousin.	C	Cd-Cx
5	*That Betty Morris is president of our class* is not unexpected.	C	Cx
6	*On a beautiful autumn afternoon* Ichabod Crane rode to the party at the home of Katrina.	prep	S
7	Ichabod was happy *as he rode toward the Van Tassel home.*	C	Cx
8	*Anticipating a delightful time,* the schoolmaster enjoyed the ride.	part	S
9	*The troubles of school forgotten,* he thought only of happiness.	abs	S
10	Even Gunpowder, *the old horse,* responded to the beauty about him.	app	S
11	Marie Curie, *the famous scientist,* endured many hardships.	app	S
12	If you are discouraged by reverses, read the life of Marie Curie, *the discoverer of radium.*	app	Cx
13	*Refusing to accept misfortune,* she struggled on to discover radium.	part	S
14	Marie Curie, *who surmounted all obstacles,* richly deserved her fame.	C	Cx
15	*Waiting patiently for his master,* the dog stands by the gate.	part	S
16	*Although his master does not return,* the dog still waits.	C	Cx
17	The dog, *a faithful friend,* still waits for his master.	app	S
18	Laura Ingalls Wilder, *the well-known writer,* wrote stories that interest young people.	app	Cx
19	*Knowing the psychology of youth,* Laura Ingalls Wilder wrote much for boys and girls.	part	S
20	Laura Ingalls Wilder, *who was a well-known author,* wrote for young people.	C	Cx

Plain English Handbook, 99, 101, 389, 390, 396, 410–416, 421.

Activity: Write five sentences; then rewrite each, varying sentence structure as was done in this lesson.

SCORE _____ (Top Score 40)

57

Sentence Weaknesses

Each item in this lesson contains a confusing reference of a pronoun, a dangling verbal modifier, a misplaced modifier, a needless shift in person, number, or voice, or parallel thoughts not in parallel form. On the line provided, rewrite each item, correcting the weaknesses. (Correct answers may vary.)

EXAMPLE: Every boy should do their own work.

Every boy should do his own work.

1 Don told Jack that he had been invited to the party.

Don said, "Jack, you have been invited to the party."

2 We campers like to swim and playing tennis.

We campers like to swim and to play tennis.

3 When we went camping, a good time was had.

When we went camping, we had a good time.

4 Ruth saw a leather coat in a shop window that she liked.

In a shop window Ruth saw a leather coat that she liked.

5 Working hard, the job was finally completed.

Working hard, we completed the job.

6 Marilyn told Louise that she would be appointed chairperson.

Marilyn said, "Louise, you will be appointed chairperson."

7 We saw some places in New Mexico that we liked.

In New Mexico we saw some places that we liked.

8 Standing on the hill, the sunrise was colorful.

Standing on the hill, they saw a colorful sunrise.

9 Each one of the girls should bring their swimming suit.

Each one of the girls should bring her swimming suit.

10 Overcoming odds is heroic, but to give up is cowardly.

Overcoming odds is heroic, but giving up is cowardly.

11 Each girl should work hard if they hope to succeed.

Each girl should work hard if she hopes to succeed.

12 Planning great things is easy, but to do them is difficult.

To plan great things is easy, but to do them is difficult.

13 Opening the door, a strange sight was seen.

Opening the door, he saw a strange sight.

14 We went to the party and a wonderful time was had.

We went to the party and had a wonderful time.

15 In the winter I like to skate and playing basketball.

In the winter I like skating and playing basketball.

Plain English Handbook, 438, 439, 450–455.

SCORE _____ (Top Score 15)

Sentence Faults

Each item in this lesson contains a comma blunder, a run-on blunder, a period fault, or ideas of unequal rank joined by **and**. Rewrite each item to improve it. Try to subordinate lesser ideas (433, 447) rather than write primer sentences (449). (Correct answers may vary.)

EXAMPLE: The speaker is here have you seen him?

The speaker is here. Have you seen him?

1 Lynda has a scholarship, she expects to attend Harvard next year.
Lynda, who has a scholarship, expects to attend Harvard next year.

2 Our president has gone to the meeting he will bring us a report.
Our president, who has gone to the meeting, will bring us a report.

3 Helen is on our debating team and she likes to listen to radio forums.
Helen, who is on our debating team, likes to listen to radio forums.

4 Bob and I finished our work. While you and Jack were away.
While you and Jack were away, Bob and I finished our work.

5 Mary Jane is a friend to everyone, all the students like her.
All the students like Mary Jane, who is a friend to everyone.

6 Rolando always does good work. Because he wants to go to college.
Rolando always does good work because he wants to go to college.

7 Betty won the race, and she is a good runner.
Betty, who is a good runner, won the race.

8 Charlotte attends law school, and she plays in a dance band, and she earns her expenses.
Charlotte, who attends law school, plays in a dance band to earn her expenses.

9 Tish likes biology she hopes to become a heart specialist.
Tish, who likes biology, hopes to become a heart specialist.

10 We enjoyed the afternoon. Especially the drive in the park.
We enjoyed the afternoon, especially the drive in the park.

11 Roberta is a talented illustrator, and she is studying medieval art.
Roberta, a talented illustrator, is studying medieval art.

12 Everyone will have a good time. When we go on the picnic.
When we go on the picnic, everyone will have a good time.

13 Ann writes poetry, and her brother is a reporter.
Ann, whose brother is a reporter, writes poetry.

14 The boys are working hard. Hoping to complete the job soon.
Hoping to complete the job soon, the boys are working hard.

15 Mary is the chairperson she will preside at the meeting.
Mary, the chairperson, will preside at the meeting.

Plain English Handbook, 433, 436, 444–447, 449.

Activity: Explain the fault of each ineffective item above.

59

Reviewing Sentence Weaknesses

Each item in this lesson contains a defective sentence. The defects are caused by needless shifts in person or number or voice, by dangling verbal modifiers, by misplaced modifiers, by run-on blunders, by parallel thoughts not in parallel form, by incorrect uses of the comma or the period, or by confusing reference of a pronoun. Rewrite each item, making all changes necessary to correct sentence weaknesses. (Correct answers may vary.)

EXAMPLE: Each boy must furnish their own ski equipment.

Each boy must furnish his own ski equipment.

1 Tom asked Dick if he thought he would be elected.
   Tom asked, "Dick, do you think you will be elected?"

2 The new sweaters are here, have you seen them?
   The new sweaters are here. Have you seen them?

3 Rita thinks hiking is more fun than to bike.
   Rita thinks hiking is more fun than biking.

4 Standing at the window, many people passed by.
   Standing at the window, I saw many people pass by.

5 Ellen has come have you seen her?
   Ellen has come. Have you seen her?

6 To fight for freedom is striving for the benefit of humanity.
   To fight for freedom is to strive for the benefit of humanity.

7 The person who spoke was Gerald Myers he is our president.
   The person who spoke was Gerald Myers, our president.

8 Strolling through the woods, a waterfall was seen.
   Strolling through the woods, we saw a waterfall.

9 Hal Brown is our captain, do you know him?
   Do you know Hal Brown, our captain?

10 Maria likes to write stories. Particularly historical stories.
   Maria likes to write stories, particularly historical ones.

11 We saw many things in the store that we wanted.
   In the store we saw many things that we wanted.

12 When we went fishing, many fish were caught.
   When we went fishing, we caught many fish.

13 Betsy and I stayed. Until the other women came.
   Betsy and I stayed until the other women came.

14 If any boy wishes to take the course you must enroll now.
   If any boy wishes to take the course, he must enroll now.

15 The coach likes to swim, he likes to skate, too.
   The coach likes to swim and to skate.

Plain English Handbook, 438, 439, 444–446, 449–455.

Activity: Analyze one of the sentences which you have rewritten. *Plain English Handbook,* 412.

SCORE _____ (Top Score 15)

Capitalization and Punctuation/1

Insert punctuation marks where they are needed; cross out each incorrect mark and place the correct mark above it. Cross out each word that is incorrectly capitalized and write the correct form above it.

EXAMPLE: Lou Williams, a ~~Sophomore~~ *sophomore* in West ~~high~~ *High* School, is the soloist. (500, 471)

1 Most of the $\overset{s}{\text{S}}$ophomores will study the following subjects: $\overset{h}{\text{H}}$istory, $\overset{E}{\text{e}}$nglish, and $\overset{g}{\text{G}}$eometry. (471, 493, 504)

2 The $\overset{s}{\text{S}}$peaker quoted from "Four $\overset{L}{\text{l}}$ittle $\overset{F}{\text{f}}$oxes," the poem by Lew Sarett. (478, 500)

3 As we listened, the minister quoted from the $\overset{B}{\text{b}}$ible and prayed for $\overset{G}{\text{g}}$od's blessing. (497, 477, 476, 519)

4 "Now is the time," the teacher said, "when you should learn good $\overset{E}{\text{e}}$nglish." (503, 468)

5 The director said, "Whenever you come, come early!" (507, 506)

6 The president (he is a senior) said that the club would be self-supporting. (526, 533)

7 When my brother goes back to $\overset{c}{\text{C}}$ollege next $\overset{f}{\text{F}}$all, he will do graduate work. (471, 470, 497)

8 "Why did you laugh," Mary asked, "when he said, 'Pardon me,' and sat down?" (515, 501, 513)

9 The famous speaker began, "There is no—" He did not finish the sentence. (501, 507, 466, 522)

10 Sue and I went to Ripton, Vermont, last $\overset{C}{\text{c}}$hristmas. $\overset{W}{\text{w}}$e stayed a week. (500, 469, 486, 464)

11 Peg met $\overset{C}{\text{c}}$olonel Shaw while she was in Boise, Idaho, last $\overset{s}{\text{S}}$pring. (481, 500, 470)

12 Did Edgar Allan Poe receive only ten dollars for "The $\overset{R}{\text{r}}$aven"? (478, 514, 529)

13 Ben asked his $\overset{m}{\text{M}}$other whether he could go to $\overset{M}{\text{m}}$exico during $\overset{M}{\text{m}}$ay. (482, 468, 469)

14 In 1986, the $\overset{A}{\text{a}}$stronomy Club went to New Zealand to see $\overset{H}{\text{h}}$alley's Comet. (471, 484, 519)

15 I have never visited the $\overset{S}{\text{s}}$outhwest; however I hope to someday. (474, 490)

16 Did Dorothy Parker write "One $\overset{P}{\text{p}}$erfect $\overset{R}{\text{r}}$ose"? (478, 514, 529)

17 Our new teacher once taught in a $\overset{h}{\text{H}}$igh $\overset{s}{\text{S}}$chool in Atlanta, Georgia. (471, 500)

18 Was the $\overset{B}{\text{b}}$attle of Gettysburg fought in the Revolutionary $\overset{W}{\text{w}}$ar? (473, 529)

19 No, my cousin doesn't work in the men's department of that store. (498, 482, 517, 519)

20 $\overset{D}{\text{d}}$id Whitman write the poem, "$\overset{W}{\text{w}}$hen Lilacs $\overset{L}{\text{l}}$ast in the $\overset{D}{\text{d}}$ooryard Bloomed"? (464, 500, 478, 514, 529)

Activity: Apply your knowledge of punctuation and capitalization to the writing of a paragraph. *Plain English Handbook,* 541–555.

SCORE _____ (Top Score 70)

LESSON 50

Capitalization and Punctuation/2

The sentences in this lesson are defective as a result of incorrect capitalization and punctuation. Cross out each word that is incorrectly capitalized and write the correct form above it. Insert all necessary punctuation marks; cross out each incorrect mark and place the correct mark above it. (In the asterisked sentences a semicolon may be used in place of the period and capital letter.)

EXAMPLE: Ben has practiced all week, Hoping to improve his backstroke.   (446)

* 1 Harold is here now, he must have come with the coach.   (444, 486, 490, 464)

2 I like football very much, what is your favorite game?   (444, 486, 464)

3 We can play a game of quoits, While the others swim.   (446, 497)

* 4 You should read this new book, it is very interesting.   (445, 486, 490, 464)

5 We saw many interesting places, When we were in the East.   (446, 497)

* 6 Chris Jordan is captain of the team, he is an excellent player.   (445, 486, 490, 464)

7 The team entered the tournament yesterday, Expecting to win the trophy.   (446, 499)

* 8 Bette swims well, she hopes to become an Olympic swimmer.   (444, 486, 490, 464)

* 9 Robert will attend Princeton, he will major in English.   (445, 486, 490, 464)

*10 I like swimming in the ocean, some people do not like it.   (445, 486, 490, 464)

*11 Mary writes well, let her write the story for the paper.   (444, 486, 490, 464)

62   *12 This is the last game of the season, we must not lose it.   (445, 486, 490, 464)

13 Who brought these grapes? they are very good.   (529, 445, 464)

14 We returned from the long trip, Feeling that it had been worthwhile.   (446, 499)

*15 Mr. Weldon is our new music director, have you met him?   (444, 486, 490, 464)

16 Our principal is in the East now, Attending an educational meeting.   (446, 499)

*17 Alice and Jane are here, the other students have gone.   (444, 486, 490, 464)

*18 My mother is a real friend, she never fails me.   (445, 486, 490, 464)

*19 This is a good story, have you read it?   (444, 486, 490, 464)

20 I like all kinds of flowers, Especially those that bloom all summer.   (446, 499)

Activity: Study the punctuation and capitalization rules in section 464–540 of *Plain English Handbook.*

SCORE _____ (Top Score 40)

LESSON 51

Using Verbs

Cross out each incorrect verb and write the correct form above it. If there is no incorrect verb, write **C** before the sentence.

EXAMPLE: Here ~~comes~~ *come* Jo and Terry, but they are too late. (239)

1 One of the girls ~~are~~ *is* here now, but the others have not come. (246, 216)

2 Nan ~~don't~~ *doesn't* know whether or not the colors for the costumes have been chosen. (197, 185)

3 Neither Claire nor Mike ~~are here~~ *is*, but here ~~comes~~ *come* Jane and Sue. (237, 239)

4 A number of the employees ~~was~~ *were* not here when we did that work. (244, 216)

5 Neither Ann nor the boys ~~was~~ *were* here when Dave and I ~~come~~ *came*. (238, 216)

6 The new club president, as well as the members, ~~were~~ *was* glad we came. (236, 216)

7 There ~~was~~ *were* about ten students in the room when the bell rang. (239, 204)

8 The others had gone to the pep rally when Tim and I ~~come~~ *came*. (204, 216)

9 The assistant coach, not the players, ~~were~~ *was* here when we came. (261, 216)

10 Fred ~~give~~ *gave* me this book on chess for you while you ~~was~~ *were* in class. (204, 260)

11 Each of the players ~~act~~ *acts* as if he ~~was~~ *were* the captain. (242, 258)

12 If I were Hank, I'd ~~lay~~ *lie* down on the grass and rest. (256, 217)

C 13 If Jill was at the meeting, she has not spoken about what was done. (257, 204)

14 Every one of the students ~~are~~ *is* proud that our senior team ~~have~~ *has* won the trophy. (242, 240)

15 Neither Joe nor Ann has seen Jim since you ~~was~~ *were* here at noon. (237, 260)

16 That student ~~don't~~ *doesn't* know that she is to bring the dues to me. (197)

17 If I ~~was~~ *were* the chairperson, I'd invite everyone who is willing to work. (256, 242, 249)

18 He is one of those people who ~~is~~ *are* never satisfied with what they have done. (241, 216)

19 Neither Mr. Howe nor the girls ~~was~~ *were* here when the barbershop quartet sang. (238, 204)

20 We had sat but a moment when the speaker rose and ~~begun~~ *began* her address. (217, 204)

63

Spelling List/8

enemies	universal	icicles	feature	monotonous
procession	feign	opposition	convenience	criticize
personally	project	forgotten	exhaustive	organized
excelled	citizens	excels	formally	qualify
orchestras	examinations	pageant	purchase	granite
commercial	readily	concrete	cooperate	opponents
gracious	exceptionally	necklace	faucet	reception
eminent	imaginary	congratulate	operators	quality

SCORE _____ (Top Score 25)

Substantives, Modifiers, Connectives

Cross out each incorrect noun, pronoun, adjective, adverb, preposition, or conjunction and write the correct form above it. If there is no incorrect word, write **C** before the sentence.

besides
EXAMPLE: There were four girls ~~beside~~ me who went swimming.   (353)

1. Helen looked proud, and she surely spoke ~~good.~~ *well* (289, 311, 329)
2. Was it Fred and ~~him~~ *he* who sent the letter to ~~we~~ *us* girls? (152, 157)
3. Most of ~~we~~ *us* other boys are taller than Mike and he. (157, 148)

C 4. It was she and I whom you saw with Carlos and him. (152, 160, 153)
5. Henry is ~~some~~ *somewhat* taller than ~~me,~~ *I* but I am the heavier. (334, 148, 296)
6. Sarah and she are the girls ~~whom~~ *who* we think will help Tom and me. (149, 160, 153)
7. Sue and she told Ann and ~~I~~ *me* to mix two ~~bucketsful~~ *bucketfuls* of water with the cement. (149, 272, 87)
8. Hal and ~~him~~ *he* should have given the notes to me. (149)
9. Jack played well, and there isn't ~~no~~ *any (or is no)* reason for him to feel bad. (329, 336, 289)
10. The principal asked Joe and me to divide the money ~~between~~ *among* the four boys. (272, 354)
11. Rachel was angry ~~at~~ *with* John for taking the bicycle without telling her. (351)

C 12. I lost the badminton racket and couldn't find it anywhere. (330)
13. Jane is not ~~as~~ *so* good at swimming as Mary and ~~me.~~ *I* (310, 148)
14. Lucille and she expect to be back home ~~inside of~~ *within* a month. (149, 356)
15. This outline is different ~~than~~ *from* the one you gave Hank and me. (337, 154)
16. Elsa and he will not go to the picnic ~~except~~ *unless* Beth and I will go with them. (149, 370)
17. If Hugh and he had behaved ~~different,~~ *differently* they might have been chosen. (149, 311)
18. Neither of the judges thinks that this is the ~~best~~ *better* of the two stories. (163, 296)
19. Are you sure it was ~~them~~ *they* who saw Kay and ~~he~~ *him* at the rodeo? (152, 153)
20. Every boy in the club will do ~~their~~ *his* best to encourage Lana and him. (164, 153)
21. It could have been they ~~who~~ *whom* you saw with Dave and her. (152, 160, 153)
22. Frank and ~~me~~ *I* will help Clair and her with the school radio program. (149, 153)
23. Tim and I have asked Dad to go with ~~we~~ *us* boys to the automobile show. (149, 157)
24. ~~Less~~ *Fewer* than sixty people have enrolled for the new sewing classes. (306)
25. We found our way to East High School ~~easy~~ *easily* last night. (339)

Activity: Give the use and case of each substantive you corrected.

SCORE _____ (Top Score 30)

Reviewing Word Usage

Cross out each incorrectly used word and write the correct form above it. If there is no incorrect word, write C before the sentence.

EXAMPLE: That boy is ~~sort of~~ *rather* quiet, isn't he?   (333)

C 1 It could have been he whom you saw with Cindy and her.   (152, 160, 153)

2 Jack is the older of the two, and he surely does skate ~~good~~ *well*.   (296, 311, 329)

3 Here ~~comes~~ *come* Solar and she to help Paolo and ~~I~~ *me* with this report.   (239, 149, 153)

4 Ted and he helped Anna and me pick twenty ~~basketsful~~ *basketfuls* of apples.   (149, 272, 87)

5 Did the ancient Egyptians believe that the earth ~~was~~ *is* round?   (251)

6 Should each girl bring ~~their~~ *her* own canteen and sleeping bag?   (142)

7 It was she who told me that you ~~was~~ *were* the leader for ~~we~~ *us* boys.   (152, 260, 157)

8 The boy ~~who~~ *whom* you saw with me is my cousin from Maine.   (160)

9 As I ~~come~~ *came* into the room, the woman who sat at the desk ~~raised~~ *rose* to her feet.   (216, 217)

10 He and I had ~~drove~~ *driven* a short distance when the rain began to fall.   (149, 204)

11 Elaine and she have done much better work than many people older than ~~them~~ *they*.   (149, 148)

12 ~~Is~~ *Are* Joe and he going with my sister and ~~I~~ *me*?   (149, 153)

13 John Ross is the older of my two ~~brother-in-laws~~ *brothers-in-law*.   (296, 86)

14 Gene and he sit ~~in back of~~ *behind* me in our English class.   (149, 217, 363)

15 Sue and he should ~~of~~ *have* helped James and her with the plans.   (149, 230, 153)

16 There are ~~less~~ *fewer* cheerleaders this year, but they surely have spirit.   (306, 311)

17 The men's ~~lifes~~ *lives* are very routine.   (122, 82)

18 It was ~~us~~ *we* boys who wanted to leave early.   (151)

19 Madeline told us to give out the ~~ten last~~ *last ten* books.   (303)

20 There ~~goes~~ *go* the girls now with Mrs. Raines and him.   (239, 153)

21 Bill and he think it is ~~me~~ *I* who ~~is~~ *am* to blame for the error.   (149, 152, 249)

22 If I ~~was~~ *were* she, I'd ask Marie and him to have some new games.   (256, 272)

23 Neither Kay nor Jorge ~~were~~ *was* here when he and I came to class.   (237, 149, 216)

24 Sam is one of those people who ~~is~~ *are* always talking at the wrong time.   (241)

25 The coach and he were greatly pleased at ~~us~~ *our* winning the big game.   (149, 270)

Activity: Give the reason for each correction you have made.

SCORE _____ (Top Score 30)

65

Review of Reviews

Cross out each incorrectly used word and write the correct form above it. If there is no incorrect word, write C before the sentence.

lives

EXAMPLE: Do you enjoy reading about the ~~lifes~~ of famous people? (82)

were
1 If I ~~was~~ she, I'd ask Hugh and her to go with Bess and him. (256, 272, 153)

she   him
2 Hal and ~~her~~ saw Ruth and ~~he~~ when they came into the room. (149, 153, 216)

have   whom
3 It could ~~of~~ been Kay ~~who~~ you saw with Susan and him. (230, 160, 153)

done
4 After we had ~~did~~ most of the work, Don and he came to help us. (216, 149)

well
5 The younger of those two boys surely plays handball ~~good~~. (296, 311, 329)

anyone (*or* is no one)
6 Henry and he say there isn't ~~no one~~ to go with Ray and me. (149, 336, 153)

gone
7 My assistants and I have filled the orders; the drivers have ~~went~~ to deliver them. (149, 216)

saw
8 When we boys ran to the corner, we ~~seen~~ the wrecked cars. (151, 216)

teach
9 The coach is trying to ~~learn~~ George and him a new play. (227, 153)

were
10 There ~~was~~ four boys who had done their work and had gone home. (239, 216)

she
11 It must have been ~~her~~ who came to the party with Ann and him. (152, 216, 153)

C 12 Elena and she will go with Jim and me to the show tomorrow. (149, 153)

doesn't
13 Fred is really the better athlete of the two, but he ~~don't~~ like hockey. (296, 197)

his
14 We students know that each of the boys will do ~~their~~ part to win. (151, 163, 242)

are   us
15 Ms. Ward is one of those teachers who ~~is~~ eager to inspire ~~we~~ students. (241, 157)

thinks
16 Each of the musicians ~~think~~ that I am responsible for the booking. (242)

were
17 There are many of us who do not think you ~~was~~ to blame for the error. (239, 260)

Were
18 ~~Was~~ Don and she here when Ken and he came? (247, 147, 216)

was
19 Five hundred dollars ~~were~~ paid to Mr. Ford for his share of the property. (245)

doesn't so
20 Jaime ~~don't~~ seem ~~as~~ tall as his younger brother. (197, 310)

as
21 You would soon get well if you would only do ~~like~~ the doctor ordered. (372)

lie
22 Mother had us children ~~lay~~ down for a nap every day when we were small. (155, 217)

should (*or omit* had)
23 Some of us boys ~~had ought to~~ help Dick and her with the luggage. (157, 225, 153)

C 24 Miss Wilson and he had not given us all the instructions when the bell rang. (149, 216)

begun   came
25 We girls had eaten breakfast and had ~~began~~ our work when Tim and he ~~come~~. (151, 204, 216)

SCORE _____ (Top Score 30)

Composition and the Use of Words

This test parallels, in content, Inventory 5, page 111.

I. *Paragraphs, Outlines, and Letters*
   (Lessons 55–60)   15 Points

Underline the bold-faced word or phrase that makes the statement true.

EXAMPLE: In dialogue each speech is (set off by dashes/<u>separately paragraphed</u>).

1 The sentences of a good paragraph are (loosely/<u>closely</u>) related in thought.
2 The topic sentence of a paragraph is (always/<u>generally</u>) at the beginning.
3 The proper arrangement of the sentences in a paragraph is (emphasis/<u>coherence</u>).
4 Unity in the paragraph means (<u>sticking to the subject</u>/proper arrangement of parts).
5 The topics of an outline should be arranged in (no special/<u>logical</u>) order.
6 The most careful writers use (many/<u>few</u>) abbreviations in letters.
7 End punctuation is (<u>necessary</u>/optional) after the salutation and close of a letter.
8 The date is the (first/<u>last</u>) item of the heading.
9 Expressions such as *beg to say* are now considered (effective/<u>obsolete</u>).
10 The mark usually placed after the salutation of a business letter is the (comma/<u>colon</u>).
11 The mark usually placed after the salutation of a friendly letter is the (dash/<u>comma</u>).
12 The participial closing is (<u>omitted</u>/much used) by modern writers.
13 (Each/<u>Only the first</u>) word of the complimentary close is capitalized.
14 The signature should be followed by (<u>no punctuation</u>/a period).
15 The business letter has (five/<u>six</u>) parts.

II. *Faulty Expressions in the Sentence*
   (Lessons 61 and 62)   10 Points

Cross out each faulty expression and write above it the correct or more appropriate one.

EXAMPLE: What kind of ~~affect~~ did the ocean have on you?   *effect*

1 If I go any ~~farther~~ with the plans, the other members will be angry.   *further*
2 My cousin is a ~~real~~ talented musician.   *really*
3 It will be a long ~~ways~~ for those girls to walk.   *way*
4 Didn't almost all the boys ~~suspicion~~ him of stealing the ball?   *suspect*
5 Because the bridge was out, that was ~~all the farther~~ we could go.   *as far as*
6 ~~Not a one~~ of them knew what was wrong with the car.   *Not one*
7 Do you know where Mother put the peanuts ~~at~~?
8 ~~Neither~~ of the three girls could think of an answer.   *None*
9 His words of warning are likely to ~~effect~~ their actions.   *affect*
10 Bob will let you have his car if it is ~~alright~~ with his father.   *all right*

III. *Using Words in the Sentence*

[Lessons 64–66]

Cross out each incorrect word and write the correct form above it. If there is no error, write **C** before the sentence.

EXAMPLE: Nell and ~~her~~ *she* picked several bucketfuls of apples.

1 Although Sarah is angry ~~at~~ *with* you, you shouldn't feel bad.

2 Doesn't he know how the thieves ~~was~~ *were* captured?

3 Here come Fred and Bill with Mary and ~~she~~ *her*.

4 Invite ~~whomever~~ *whoever* will help Ruth and her.

5 Although the pie didn't look ~~well~~ *good*, it tasted good.

6 Neither her gloves nor her coat ~~were~~ *was* different from mine.

7 June is one of those workers who ~~is~~ *are* never satisfied.

8 The president, not the members, ~~are~~ *is* responsible.

9 If she ~~was~~ *were* you, she would sit down and say nothing.

10 He cannot do differently ~~except~~ *unless* we help him.

11 As the boat ~~sunk~~ *sank*, the crew swam to the island.

C 12 It was probably they who left us boys the tickets.

13 As soon as I ~~seen~~ *saw* him, I gave him your message.

14 You ~~was~~ *were* here when she told us about Betina's entering the contest.

15 The sun had already ~~raised~~ *risen* when we ate breakfast.

16 Neither Alice nor Ann would lend ~~their~~ *her* book.

17 Do you feel that you can do ~~like~~ *as* we do?

18 ~~Was~~ *Were* you there when Jack and I came?

19 Are Joe and Bert coming with Diane and ~~she~~ *her*?

C 20 Doris and she surely feel bad about it.

21 ~~Except~~ *Unless* you come, Jake is likely to stay at home.

C 22 I am sure that whomever you invite will go with Tom and him.

23 The taller of the two lamps is the ~~best~~ *better* one to use while reading.

24 All ~~us~~ *we* seniors bought our sweaters at Howell and Dunn's store.

C 25 Was it he whom you helped?

68

SCORE _____ (Top Score 50)

LESSON 55

Paragraph, Précis, and Outline

Underline the bold-faced word or phrase that makes the statement true.

EXAMPLE: There are (**six**/**four**) types of expression known as forms of discourse. (551)

1 A paragraph develops (**only one topic**/**several topics**). (541)

2 A topic (**may**/**may not**) be developed in more than one paragraph. (541)

3 In dialogue each speech is (**separately paragraphed**/**set off by dashes**). (542)

4 One sentence (**always expresses**/**does not always express**) the topic. (544)

5 The topic sentence is placed (**at the end of**/**anywhere in**) the paragraph. (544)

6 There (**is only one way**/**are many ways**) to develop a topic. (545)

7 Giving stress to important ideas in a paragraph is called (**emphasis**/**coherence**). (550)

8 Sticking to the subject is called (**emphasis**/**unity**). (548)

9 The correct arrangement of sentences in a paragraph is (**unity**/**coherence**). (549)

10 The form of discourse used in explaining is called (**description**/**exposition**). (552)

11 Picturing in words is called (**description**/**narration**). (553)

12 The form of discourse used in telling a story is (**argumentation**/**narration**). (554)

13 A précis is (**more**/**less**) precise than a paraphrase. (558)

14 A good précis retains (**none**/**all**) of the thought of the original. (558)

15 Précis writing is good for those who use too (**few**/**many**) words in writing. (559)

16 A good précis (**retains**/**changes**) the order of the thought of the original. (559)

17 In writing a précis, one should use (**one's own words**/**the words of the original**). (559)

18 Clear and forceful sentences are (**optional**/**necessary**) in précis writing. (558)

19 The topics in an outline should be arranged in (**irregular**/**logical**) order. (578)

20 The main topics of an outline are marked by (**Roman numerals**/**Arabic numbers**). (579)

Activities: Practice in the writing of précis is an excellent aid in developing the ability to write well. Read 557–560 in *Plain English Handbook,* and then select a short article you wish to condense. Try to reduce the number of words to one third of the original word count. Retain all the meaning of the original text. Write a paragraph on the value of knowing how to write good letters.

SCORE _____ (Top Score 20)

69

Letter Writing

Underline the bold-faced word or phrase that makes the statement true.

EXAMPLE: The business letter has (**five**/<u>**six**</u>) parts.   (590)

1 Letters are broadly divided into (**four**/<u>**two**</u>) general classes.   (586)
2 A letter (<u>**may**</u>/**may not**) combine both business and social purposes.   (586)
3 A business letter (**need not be**/<u>**should be**</u>) answered promptly.   (589)
4 The heading should be at the upper (**left-hand**/<u>**right-hand**</u>) side of the paper.   (591)
5 Careful letter-writers abbreviate (<u>**little**</u>/**much**) in headings.   (591)
6 The date is the (**first**/<u>**last**</u>) item in the heading.   (592)
7 The inside address of a business letter is placed (<u>**at**</u>/**near**) the left margin.   (594)
8 The inside address may be omitted from a (<u>**social**</u>/**business**) letter.   (617)
9 End punctuation is (**required**/<u>**not required**</u>) in the heading and inside address.   (593)
10 The (**heading**/**inside address**) contains the address of the writer.   (591)
11 The salutation should be below the inside address (**near**/<u>**at**</u>) the left margin.   (595)
12 The form of the salutation (<u>**should**</u>/**need not**) be consistent with the type of letter.   (595)
13 If the word *dear* is preceded by the word *my* in a salutation, both words (**are**/<u>**are not**</u>) capitalized.   (596)
14 A close such as *I remain* is now considered (**effective**/<u>**obsolete**</u>).   (599)
15 The (**comma**/<u>**colon**</u>) is used after the salutation of a business letter.   (597)
16 The (<u>**comma**</u>/**dash**) is properly used after the salutation of a friendly letter.   (617)
17 The style of a letter of friendship should be (<u>**conversational**</u>/**formal**).   (617)
18 A good business letter (<u>**should**</u>/**need not**) be clear, concise, and courteous.   (589)
19 (**Each**/<u>**Only the first**</u>) word of the complimentary close is capitalized.   (599)
20 The participial closing is (<u>**never**</u>/**much**) used by the best writers.   (599)
21 The only mark used after the complimentary close is the (**period**/<u>**comma**</u>).   (599)
22 The signature should be written (<u>**legibly**</u>/**with a flourish**).   (600)
23 The signature (<u>**may**</u>/**may not**) be typed beneath the longhand form.   (600)
24 The informal invitation follows the form of the (<u>**social**</u>/**business**) letter.   (617)
25 The formal invitation is always written in (**first**/<u>**third**</u>) person.   (623)

Spelling List/9

audio	mobilize	economy	siege	quarantine
mediator	unsaturated	intimate	medieval	symbol
scientific	mezzanine	permanent	immaterial	characteristic
metropolitan	queue	consistent	quotient	persuasion
Hawaiian	apricot	acceptance	catastrophe	resources
jovial	apparatus	individual	substitutes	inadequate
vertebra	tariff	criticism	lenient	marvelous
apropos	medium	invalid	device	prophecy

SCORE _____ (Top Score 25)

The Business Letter

Make all necessary corrections of the letter parts. Insert needed punctuation marks, and correct errors in spelling and capitalization by crossing out the incorrect word and writing the correct form above it. If something is in the wrong place, indicate the correct position by arrows.

1   May 10, 19——

2   537 Crestway Ave, *nue*

3   Clarksville, Nebraska 68005

4   Mr. George J. Holmes

5   1735 East Grand *S*treet

6   Lincoln, ~~Neb.~~ *Nebraska* 68508

7   Dear Mr. Holmes:

8   I read in the *C*larksville *C*hronicle that you were looking for a sound ~~technicien~~ *technician*

9   when Sherlock and the *H*olmes Gang goes on ~~it's~~ *its* *E*ast Coast tour this summer.

10   I would like you to consider me for the job.

11   I am eighteen years old and a senior at Clarksville *H*igh. I have been in charge of

12   *S*ound at *S*chool assemblies and for three ~~musicles~~ *musicals* produced in school. I have also played bass

13   for the past two years in a local band, the Marbles. We have played at high school dances

14   throughout the county.

15   I would like to work for your band, first of all, because I admire it.

16   Second, I'm seriously interested in a career as a sound engineer, and the experience

17   would be very helpful. I want to major in communications in *c*ollege and hope to work

18   for a college radio station.

19   I can give you references on ~~reguest.~~ *request*

20   I'd be happy to see you for an ~~intervew~~ *interview* at your ~~conveneince.~~ *convenience*

21   Yours *V*ery *T*ruly,

                                 Robert Gordon

22   Robert Gordon

Plain English Handbook, 468, 470, 471, 474, 478, 481, 487, 500, 502, 591–595, 597–600.

Activity: Write a business letter. Select the type of letter you wish to write from the list in *Plain English Handbook,* 604.

SCORE _____ (Top Score 25)

71

The Letter of Inquiry

Make the necessary changes in capitalization, punctuation, spelling, and usage to correct the letter.

1   110 **S**outh Main Street

2   Madison, Wisconsin 53702

3   November 5, 19_____

4   Mr. Hank Christopher

5   230 Randal Road

6   Belmont, California 94002

7   Dear **M**~~m~~r. Christopher:

8   The Percy **H**~~h~~igh **S**~~s~~chool Band is going to hold an auction on **S**~~s~~aturday afternoon,

9   April 23. Our goal is to ~~raze~~ **raise** money for new uniforms. If you remember what they

10   were like when you were here, you'll agree that we need them. Our ~~cheif~~ **chief** auction item

11   is a rare record you made when you were still a student here. **T**~~t~~hat is why

12   I'm writing.

13   Since you will be giving a concert in **M**~~m~~adison that weekend, we ~~was~~ **were** wondering

14   if you would auction off the record yourself? **Almost** ~~Most~~ everyone at school ~~are~~ **is** a fan of yours.

15   Your being at the auction would ~~certinly~~ **certainly** draw the crowd we need for a successful auction.

16   If you are interested, please drop us a note. We would gladly work the

17   auction around your busy ~~skedule~~ **schedule**.

18   Yours **truly**~~truely~~,

19   *Frances Bauer*

20   Frances Bauer

                                               President, Percy **H**~~h~~igh **S**~~s~~chool Band

Plain English Handbook, 164, 197, 204, 217, 328, 464, 468, 469, 471, 481, 486, 487, 494, 497, 500, 502, 529, 591, 600.

Activity: Write a letter of inquiry. Read *Plain English Handbook,* 607, for information concerning the letter of inquiry. Study 589–603 for the requirements and correct form of the business letter.

SCORE _____ (Top Score 25)

LESSON 59

The Friendly Letter

Make the necessary changes in capitalization, punctuation, and usage to correct the letter.

1   Parkdale camp (C)

2   Clear lake (L), minnesota (M) 55319

3   July 15, 19——

4   Dear Beverly,

5   This is certainly the most peculiarest (peculiar) camp I've ever saw (seen).

6   When I arrived, I couldn't believe dad (D) talked me into it. It's a

7   camp for computers! I mean, it's for kids, but we learn how to

8   program computers. This may not sound like the typical sort of

9   camp, but it's really not that different after all. The food is

10   still terrible, so I know it's a true-blue summer camp. In addition,

11   there is (are) hiking, swimming, and other sports, besides computer Programming (p).

12   The computers are more interesting than I thought they would

13   be. Some of the kids have devised some real (really) clever computer games.

14   We can play the games without spending bagsful (bagfuls) of quarters the

15   way we do at tom's (T) pizzeria (P). Dad suggested I come here because he

16   thought programming would be a kind of (rather) good thing to learn if I'm

17   still interested in a career in Math (m). Beside (Besides), he can be very con-

18   vincing when he starts lecturing on the importance of doing different

19   things. he's (H) gotten me into more stranger situations than this one!

20   I've made some friends here. Jeff is a brain but a very funny

21   person. Linda reminds me of you. she's (S) a sci-fi nut, too. We hope to

22   program a computer to do most (almost) all of our homework next year.

23   Have a good time on your trip. I'll see you this Fall (f) back

24   at central (C) High school (S).

25   Love,

26   Marla

Plain English Handbook, 87, 197, 204, 216, 239, 246, 294, 295, 311, 328, 333, 353, 464, 468, 470, 471, 474, 482, 495, 496, 497, 500, 502, 517, 531, 593, 600, 617.

73

SCORE _____ (Top Score 32)

The Letter of Congratulation

This note of congratulation contains errors in capitalization, punctuation, usage, and spelling. Correct the errors.

1   475 Riverview ~~d~~^Drive

2   Livermore Falls, Maine 04254

3   May 26, 19_____

4   Dear Roberta~~:~~,

5   It wasn't ~~no~~ *any (or was no)* surprise to me to read in the evening paper ~~where~~ *that*

6   you have just ~~recieved~~ *received* a Summerfield Scholarship. Your hard work in

7   ~~J~~^junior and ~~S~~^senior ~~H~~^high ~~S~~^school has brought you this honor, which you

8   so well deserve. I am especially pleased to know that your scholastic

9   record alone did not win this ~~here~~ award for you. Your exemplary char-

10   acter and pleasing personality ~~was~~ *were* contributing factors, I am sure.

11   Although I hope to see you soon, I felt ~~like~~ *that* I ~~had ought to~~ *should (or ought to)* write

12   tonight to express my congratulations to you. I wish you every success

13   in the four years of ~~C~~^college that the scholarship provides. You are

14   one ~~whom~~ *who* I think, will make the most of this opportunity, and I predict

15   great success for you in ~~you're~~ *your* ~~E~~^engineering program.

16   Sincerely ~~Y~~^yours,

17   *Tom Brooks*

Plain English Handbook, 146, 160, 225, 247, 336, 372, 380, 468, 471, 473, 484, 497, 500, 517, 591–601, 617, 622, 674.

Spelling List/10

anonymous	vermin	cemetery	considerably	counterfeit
conciliate	lethargy	referendum	encyclopedia	forcible
eminent	emphatic	laboratory	maneuver	perspiration
heritage	conceivable	minimum	reversible	picnicking
journalism	decorum	acquaintance	inflammable	susceptible
leotard	aggravate	bachelor	masquerade	hypocrite
refrain	treasurer	definition	principally	effective
subordinate	artificial	changeable	superfluous	syndicate

SCORE _____ (Top Score 25)

Faulty Expressions in the Sentence/1

In the following sentences are expressions that should be replaced by more appropriate words for formal writing. Cross out each faulty or incorrect expression and write the correct form above it.

EXAMPLE: Not *one* a one of us knew about it.

1 My father's family *raised* reared hogs on a farm near Topton, Pennsylvania.

2 His testimony in court is *likely* liable to *affect* effect the jury.

3 He doesn't know that it is only a little *way* ways to the main highway.

4 We were *very* awful tired; therefore, we could walk no *farther* further.

5 Although Bob is not so *credulous* credible as Sue, he is easily fooled.

6 *None* None of the four children wanted *further* farther work in the garden.

7 *Almost* Most all the girls have finished their work.

8 She would not let me say anything *further* farther about the matter.

9 He drives that car *well* good for one who has just learned.

10 The mayor greeted *fewer* less people *formally* formerly at this year's reception than at last year's.

11 It was surely *strange* funny that the criminal gave himself up.

12 I *suppose* expect he is not so well informed as Jim.

13 Gloria did not *suspect* suspicion that Joan was angry with her.

14 Why don't you *sit* set here while I try to *repair* fix the car?

15 I *suppose* suspect that Ann will teach you to play backgammon.

16 We *suspected* suspicioned him of telling a lie.

17 The roads are *likely* liable to be in bad condition after the rain.

18 We'll *organize* get up a social evening for the new members with *invitations as* invites like you suggested.

19 Do you feel that it is *all right* alright for me to go now?

20 He ate his meal *as if* like he hadn't had anything to eat for a week.

Plain English Handbook, 665–674.

SCORE _____ (Top Score 25)

LESSON 62

Faulty Expressions in the Sentence/2

In the following sentences cross out each faulty or informal expression and write above it the form that would be appropriate in formal writing.

likely
EXAMPLE: If we boys work hard, we are ~~liable~~ to succeed.

affect
1 How did the announcement ~~effect~~ that woman in the corner?

suppose
2 I ~~expect~~ you know that Doris is angry with us.

strange
3 Isn't it ~~funny~~ that Jane should feel so bad about it?

person
4 Tom and Mike met an interesting ~~party~~ at a ranch in New Mexico.

suppose   teach
5 I ~~expect~~ his uncle will ~~learn~~ him more about the business.

effect
6 We are hoping that the leaders will be able to ~~affect~~ a compromise.

7 Where is he aiming that rifle ~~at~~?

farther
8 Doesn't he live ~~further~~ from school than I do?

suspect
9 No one would ever ~~suspicion~~ Bert of doing a dishonest thing.

suppose   angry
10 I ~~expect~~ Harold is ~~mad~~ because I wouldn't lend him my pen.

all right   bad
11 This book is torn ~~alright;~~ it looks ~~badly.~~

12 Not ~~a~~ one of us thought it was warm enough to go swimming.

all together
13 We can ride ~~altogether~~ on our bicycles.

should (*or omit* had)   further
14 We officers ~~had ought~~ to discuss this topic ~~farther.~~

suppose
15 I ~~expect~~ that Ann will go out as soon as she arrives in New York.

Almost   further
16 ~~Most~~ all of us want to proceed ~~farther~~ with the matter.

very (*or* really)
17 John can speak ~~real~~ well.

enthusiastic
18 She was ~~enthused~~ about her trip to Japan and China.

all right
19 We wanted to make sure that everything was ~~alright~~ before we left.

at
20 We expected Fred to conduct the games, but he had to stay ~~to~~ home.

Plain English Handbook, 665–674.

SCORE _____ (Top Score 25)

Punctuation and Capitalization Review

Make all necessary changes in punctuation and capitalization to correct the sentences. Each item properly marked counts two points. (In the asterisked sentences a semicolon may be used in place of the period and capital letter.)

The

EXAMPLE: We drove to Mexico. ~~the~~ highways were good all the way.   (445, 486, 464)

* 1 That author writes unusually good stories. I have read many of them.   (445, 486, 464, 490)

2 We parked at the airport, *expecting* ~~Expecting~~ their plane to arrive momentarily.   (446, 499)

* 3 This is a perfect fall day for a picnic, *Everyone* ~~everyone~~ should be here.   (444, 486, 464)

* 4 We ought to do it now, *This* ~~this~~ might be our last opportunity.   (445, 486, 464, 490)

5 Miss Albright writes amusing limericks, *She* ~~she~~ is very talented.   (444, 486, 464)

6 Margarita is always punctual, *Some* ~~some~~ students are always late.   (444, 486, 464)

7 Our superintendent is a noted educator, *Have* ~~have~~ you ever met her?   (444, 486, 464)

* 8 Terry is one of my best friends, *She* ~~she~~ is in my history class.   (444, 486, 464, 490)

9 Jack and I went swimming, *while* ~~While~~ the other boys fished.   (446, 497)

*10 Ralph hopes to win a scholarship, *He* ~~he~~ is surely working hard.   (444, 486, 464, 490)

11 Fred is studying very hard now, *hoping* ~~Hoping~~ to pass the next test.   (446, 499)

12 The children always liked the games, *especially* ~~Especially~~ the outdoor games.   (446, 499)

13 Ricardo is sure to win the prize, *because* ~~Because~~ he always does his best.   (446, 497)

14 Ann and I pitched horseshoes, *until* ~~Until~~ the others came.   (446, 497)

*15 We surely had a good time, *You* ~~you~~ should have been there.   (444, 486, 464)

*16 Allen is planning the charity bazaar, *He* ~~he~~ will tell us about it.   (444, 486, 464)

17 Helen is going to Yale next year, *Where* ~~where~~ are you going to college?   (444, 486, 464)

* 18 Miss Dorn is the advisor for our class, *She* ~~she~~ is always ready to help anyone.   (444, 486, 464, 490)

19 We are all working hard these days, *realizing* ~~Realizing~~ that our opportunity is great.   (446, 499)

20 Rita da Costa is a very intelligent girl, *Do* ~~do~~ you know her?   (444, 486, 464)

77

Activity: Classify each sentence as **simple**, **compound**, or **complex**.

SCORE _____ (Top Score 39)

Using Words: General Review/1

Make all necessary corrections in the use of words in this lesson.

EXAMPLE: The ~~smallest~~ *smaller* of the two boys is the ~~oldest~~ *older*. (296)

1 I cannot guess ~~whom~~ *who* it was unless it was ~~him~~ *he*. (159, 152)

2 ~~Was~~ *Were* you there when we heard about ~~Shirley~~ *Shirley's* selling her story? (260, 127)

3 ~~Us~~ *We* girls will welcome ~~whoever~~ *whomever* you and ~~her~~ *she* are recommending. (151, 162, 149)

4 That old car of ~~our's~~ *ours* is certainly different ~~than their's~~ *from theirs*. (146, 337)

5 The players, as well as the director, ~~is~~ *are* eager to begin rehearsal for the new show. (236)

6 Tell me about ~~Barbara~~ *Barbara's* winning the prize for her latest ~~childrens' storys~~ *children's stories*. (127, 122, 80)

7 The two ~~Henries~~ *Henrys* fed several ~~handsful~~ *handfuls* of carrots to the ~~donkies~~ *donkeys*. (80, 87, 81)

8 We ~~couldn't~~ *could* hardly hear her, but we could tell that she was ~~mad~~ *angry*. (336, 671)

9 ~~These~~ *This* kind of light bulb ~~are~~ *is* better than that ~~there~~ kind. (302, 197, 674)

10 Neither Sally ~~or~~ *nor* Lana ~~have~~ *has* written to ~~we~~ *us* girls. (378, 237, 157)

11 They ~~had ought to~~ *should (or ought to)* teach us the correct use of those difficult verbs. (225)

12 If I had only ~~knew~~ *known* that you had no ride, I would ~~of~~ *have* taken you. (204, 230)

13 My cousin ~~begun~~ *began* the program with a guitar solo. (204)

14 There ~~goes~~ *go* Jack and ~~her~~ *she* in their ~~brother's-in-law~~ *brother-in-law's* sports car. (239, 149, 123)

15 Dick is doing ~~some~~ *somewhat* better in his work, but he still is not doing very ~~good~~ *well*. (334, 329)

16 ~~Most~~ *Almost* all of ~~we~~ *us* students will agree ~~with~~ *to* the principal's plan. (328, 157, 350)

17 The large and small calendars ~~is~~ *are* on ∧*the* library wall. (305, 248)

18 Either the girls or Miss Garcia ~~are~~ *is* to go with Tomás and ~~I~~ *me*. (238, 153)

19 The team ~~is~~ *are* to receive ~~its~~ *their* new sweaters before the next game. (240, 165)

20 ~~Was~~ *Were* the ~~turkies~~ *turkeys* roosting on the ~~rooves~~ *roofs* of the sheds? (197, 81, 83)

21 He should return the dictionary to Fred and ~~I~~ *me*. (153)

22 The number of new students enrolling in our school this year ~~are~~ *is* great. (244)

23 My ~~sister-in-laws~~ *sisters-in-law* receive high ~~salarys~~ *salaries* as engineers for this ~~states'~~ *state's* new project. (86, 80, 120)

24 He is one of those persons who always ~~tries~~ *try* to be different ~~than~~ *from* others. (241, 337)

25 His ~~aunt~~ *aunt's* and uncle's eyes are blue, but his ~~fathers'~~ *father's* eyes are brown. (125, 120)

SCORE _____ (Top Score 55)

Using Words: General Review/2

Make all necessary corrections in the use of words in this lesson.

EXAMPLE: The cake didn't ~~raise~~ *rise* very well, but we ~~eat~~ *ate* it anyway.   (217, 204)

1 Was the penknife ~~broke~~ *broken* when you ~~give~~ *gave* it to Bob and ~~he~~ *him*?   (204, 216, 153)

2 It was ~~her~~ *she* who met Jane and *me* I̶ at the airport.   (152, 153)

3 Don and ~~her give~~ *she gave* the horse two ~~bucketsful~~ *bucketfuls* of oats.   (149, 204, 216, 87)

4 If you ~~was~~ *were* the principal, what would you advise ~~we~~ *us* students to do?   (256, 155)

5 ~~Them~~ *Those* carpenters surely need any kind of work ~~bad.~~ *badly*   (442, 311)

6 She ~~done~~ *did* it exactly ~~like~~ *as* her advisor told her to do it.   (204, 216, 372)

7 Our teacher gave ~~she~~ *her* and *me* I̶ extra credit for our special conservation project.   (154)

8 Bob and ~~her sure~~ *she surely* draw ~~different than~~ *differently from* the other students.   (149, 311, 337)

9 ~~Was~~ *Were* you here when Joan ~~come~~ *came* to get the ~~cherrys~~ *cherries*?   (260, 204, 216, 80)

10 John brought five bushels of ~~potatos~~ *potatoes* from his two ~~brother-in-laws'~~ *brothers-in-law's* farm.   (78, 86, 123)

11 It must have been ~~her~~ *she* who ~~done~~ *did* the painting on display.   (152, 204, 216)

12 All ~~us~~ *we* girls ~~was~~ *were* in ~~Brown's~~ *Brown* and Lane's Store today.   (151, 197, 124)

13 We were surprised to learn of ~~Tom~~ *Tom's* winning the ~~largest~~ *larger* of the two prizes.   (270, 296)

14 Neither Esther ~~or~~ *nor* Nell ~~were~~ *was* in science class today.   (378, 237)

15 Twenty-five dollars ~~are~~ *is* too much to pay for that kind of felt hat.   (245)

16 It must have been ~~him~~ *he* and ~~her who~~ *she whom* you met outside.   (152, 149, 160)

17 We are ~~liable~~ *likely* to have ~~less~~ *fewer* failures this semester than last.   (671, 306)

18 ~~Has~~ *Have* Clara and her sister ~~went~~ *gone* to the meeting yet?   (247, 204, 216)

19 Is it Sonya or ~~me~~ *I* who ~~were~~ *was* picked?   (152, 197)

20 If I ~~was him,~~ *were he,* I should invite ~~whomever~~ *whoever* would come.   (256, 152, 161)

21 Why don't you and ~~her set~~ *she sit* with Grace and ~~I~~ *me*?   (149, 204, 217, 153)

22 Each man ~~who~~ *whom* you ask should bring ~~their~~ *his* own lunch.   (160, 142)

23 She ~~had ought to learn~~ *should (or ought to) teach* us to do ~~them~~ *those* problems.   (225, 227, 168)

24 ~~Don't~~ *Doesn't* he think that the criminal is guilty?   (197)

25 There ~~sits~~ *sit* the guides ~~who~~ *whom* we ~~seen~~ *saw* at the natural history museum.   (239, 160, 204, 216)

79

SCORE _____ (Top Score 59)

Using Words: General Review/3

Make all necessary corrections in the use of words in this lesson.

               she are
EXAMPLE: The boys, not ~~her, is~~ arranging the club's transportation. (149, 261)

1 ~~He~~ *He* and ~~her~~ *she* cannot succeed in this venture ~~except~~ *unless* we help them. (149, 370)

2 She felt ~~real~~ *very (or really)* glad about ~~Jim~~ *Jim's* winning the music award. (311, 270)

3 The child fell off ~~of~~ the pier and ~~in~~ *into* the deep water. (364, 357)

4 It could have been ~~them~~ *they* who were thought to be ~~us.~~ *we* (152, 274)

5 If Harry ~~don't~~ *doesn't* agree with ~~we~~ *us* boys, we may ~~leave~~ *let* him stay ~~to~~ *at* home. (197, 157, 227, 674)

6 ~~A~~ *An* eagle is a large predatory bird ~~who~~ *which (or that)* can fly very high. (286, 141)

7 The ~~youngest~~ *younger* of the two children seemed ~~sort of~~ *rather (or somewhat)* shy and timid. (296, 333)

8 Jane does not know ~~if she~~ *whether* she can vote or not, but she does agree ~~with~~ *to* our plan. (381, 350)

9 ~~Us~~ *We* girls thought you to be ~~she.~~ *her* (151, 273)

10 ~~Was~~ *Were* Marie and her sister with you and ~~he~~ *him* at the game? (247, 153)

11 Divide the peaches ~~between~~ *among* the four children to ~~learn~~ *teach* them to be fair. (354, 227)

12 Our freshman football team ~~have~~ *has* won all ~~their~~ *its* games this year. (92, 240, 165)

13 The ~~lifes~~ *lives* of the ~~heros was~~ *heroes were* always in danger. (82, 78, 197)

14 Is it ~~us~~ *we* girls ~~whom~~ *who* you think should make the plans? (151, 160)

15 There ~~comes~~ *come* Don and Carlo with ~~them~~ *those* girls ~~who~~ *whom* we met yesterday. (239, 442, 160)

16 Mother will not ~~leave~~ *let* us ~~lay~~ *lie* on the bed ~~except~~ *unless* we take off the spread. (227, 204, 217, 370)

17 If I ~~was her,~~ *were she* I should do ~~like~~ *as* I was told. (256, 152, 372)

18 There isn't ~~no~~ *any (or is no)* time for us boys to ~~set~~ *sit* here in idleness. (336, 204, 217)

19 No one ~~beside~~ *besides* Mr. Snyder ~~knowed~~ *knew* of our plans. (353, 204)

20 You and ~~her~~ *she* should ~~of excepted~~ *have accepted* the invitation. (149, 230, 228)

21 Each of the boys ~~were~~ *was* there to do ~~their~~ *his* share of the clean-up work. (163, 246, 142)

22 Had the bell already rung when you and he ~~come~~ *came* to class? (204)

23 She feels ~~badly~~ *bad* because her story is not ~~as~~ *so* good as ~~Janes.~~ *Jane's* (312, 310, 120)

24 ~~Most~~ *Almost* all the money was divided ~~between~~ *among* Ellen, Arthur, and ~~I.~~ *me* (328, 354, 153)

25 Each of the new women ~~have~~ *has* done ~~good~~ *well* in selling ~~their~~ *her* tickets. (163, 246, 329, 142)

SCORE _____ (Top Score 60)

Vocabulary Study/1

Here is an exercise to give you practice in detecting meaning from context (696). The sentences in the exercise are taken from magazine articles. The words that may be unfamiliar to you are italicized. The context for each word is only a sentence or two, but it should be enough to give you a clue to meaning. On the lines provided, write what you think the italicized words mean. Check your definitions by consulting the dictionary (686).

1 When a bear got into the cattle range, they dogged him *relentlessly* until they tracked him down or drove him deep into the wilder regions where the cattle never ranged.

with unyielding harshness

2 Someone from the other side of town, aware of Rocky's even disposition, tried to *goad* him into losing his temper during a football game.

drive or spur on

3 To keep the fishing boats from slipping through and laying mines required the Task Force to maintain a constant *vigil*, day and night.

wakeful watching

4 I was *skeptical*, for I just couldn't believe that so many brilliant, stationary fireballs could appear in such a concentrated area in so short a period.

doubtful

5 The differences between the original and the forgery are so slight as to be almost *imperceptible* to anyone except an expert.

not capable of being perceived

6 Mr. Messer's *antipathy* toward bears and his willingness to do them violence are shared by a dozen of his cattle-raising neighbors.

strong dislike (of)

7 Even the most renowned playwrights are not *immune* to the caustic criticism of newspaper reviewers.

exempt (from)

8 The nightmare of the railroads is financial collapse. As things stand now, the railroads are plunging downhill toward *insolvency*.

state of being unable to pay one's debts

9 There is much air traffic that we cannot do much about. Clearly we must not *tamper* with military flights.

meddle

10 Once the minerals of this desert state were *depleted*, it had little chance of prosperity and hardly enough people to maintain a state government.

destroyed or consumed

SCORE _____ (Top Score 10)

Vocabulary Study/2

Our English word *migrate* means "to go from one place to another." Once you learn this word, it is easy to learn words related to it: *migration, migrant, migratory, immigrate, immigrant, immigration, emigrate, emigrant, emigration.* If you learn words ten at a time instead of one at a time, you can build a vocabulary easily and rapidly.

We borrowed the word *migrate* from the Latin word *migratus* ("transferred"). The prefix *im* means "in" and *e* means "out." We have borrowed thirty to forty percent of our words from Latin. If you learn just a few of these Latin words, you can learn hundreds of words built from them. You can learn words at even a faster rate than ten at a time.

Five Latin roots are listed below. (In language study a *root* is the base of a word.) The meaning of each root is given. Then several of the English words built from the root are listed. Your teacher may have you supply more examples and then check the derivations in the dictionary.

Latin Roots

Root	Meaning	English Derivatives
aud, audit	hear	audience, auditorium, audible
fac, fact, fect, fic	do, make	factory, defect, efficient
scrib, script	write	describe, subscribe, manuscript
spec, spect	look, see	inspect, spectacular, spectacles
tract	draw, pull	tractor, extract, subtract

The English derivatives given as examples are all familiar words. Other derivatives for the Latin roots may not be in your vocabulary. Write the meaning of each derivative. Use your dictionary if necessary. Your teacher may call upon you to use the words in sentences.

82

aud, audit
1 audition _a hearing, especially to try out as a speaker or musical performer_
2 audiometer _an instrument for measuring the power of hearing_
3 auditory _pertaining to the sense of hearing_

fac, fact, fect, fic
4 proficient _skilled in doing or making_
5 facile _easy to do_
6 facsimile _an exact copy (made the same)_

scrib, script
7 inscribe _to write or engrave on_
8 scribble _to write hastily or carelessly_
9 prescription _written directions for medicine_

spec, spect
10 circumspect _cautious (looking about before acting)_
11 spectral _ghostly (seen, though not existing)_
12 spectator _one who sees or watches_

tract
13 protract _to draw out or lengthen in time_
14 retract _to draw back_
15 traction _act of drawing or being drawn, the force exerted in drawing_

SCORE _____ (Top Score 15)

Vocabulary Study/3

One of the best ways to build a vocabulary is to develop an interest in words. That is what the writer of this essay has done. Words to her are a source of humor, too.

Dictionary Double Talk

With almost twenty thousand words to remember, I certainly can't be blamed for mixing up one or two once in a while, can I? I'm sure that if my vocabulary were composed of two or three hundred words, I'd not make the slightest error. Never, never would I have said, "Oh, Jane, don't be obese!" when I meant "obtuse"; I should not now be blushing to recall that once I told our pastor that a guest speaker certainly had a belligerent voice, when actually I thought it was benevolent.

I used to wonder about possible connections between words that sounded alike. Did people call a sale of odd, useless things a bazaar because all the things sold there were so bizarre? If so, would it follow that a magnate was one who made magnets? This seemed logical, for I had heard news commentators mention steel magnates quite frequently. I abandoned my theory, however, when I learned that pears grew one on a stem and not in pairs.

It is sometimes difficult to change words from negative to positive form. Why is not a well-mannered person no longer "couth," if one with poor manners is uncouth? Why doesn't a capable person do things "eptly," if a clumsy person does them ineptly? Changing from positive to negative presents some weighty problems, too. I'm sure, for instance, that something which is not sincere is called insincere, but, illogically, the word meaning "not flammable" is certainly not *inflammable*. Likewise, immoderate means "without moderation," but *impassioned* is not synonymous with "without passion."

Please, oh please, will someone solve my utter dilemma about chickens? Why on earth is undressing them called "dressing"? — RAE BERG, East High School, Rockford, Illinois

To appreciate the humor of "Dictionary Double Talk" you must know the meaning of the words the writer mentions. This lesson will test your knowledge of these words.

Underline the word or phrase that means the same or nearly the same as the italicized word. Use the dictionary to check your answers.

1 *obese* — a) slow, b) very fat, c) well-dressed, d) very thin

2 *obtuse* — a) clumsy, b) out of date, c) plain, d) stupid

3 *belligerent* — a) flippant, b) hostile, c) loud, d) sad

4 *benevolent* — a) kind, b) cruel, c) sarcastic, d) sharp

5 *bizarre* — a) expensive, b) old, c) fantastic, d) cheap

6 *magnate* — a) person of industrial prominence, b) public civil officer, c) one skilled in magic, d) magnet manufacturer

7 *flammable* — a) slow to burn, b) gaudy, c) shiny, d) easily set afire

8 *inflammable* — a) slow to burn, b) gaudy, c) shiny, d) easily set afire

9 *impassioned* — a) lacking passion, b) emotionless, c) full of passion, d) violent

10 *synonymous* — a) musical, b) artificial, c) opposite, d) alike

SCORE _____ (Top Score 10)

Vocabulary Study/4

Each sentence may be completed in five different ways. Underline the phrase that best illustrates the meaning of the italicized word in each sentence.

1 One thing to do with a *knoll* is (a) shoot it, (b) sweep it under the rug, (c) report it to the police, (d) save it to show your grandchildren, (e) <u>climb it</u>.

2 A *passé* sport (a) requires a great deal of skill, (b) is played outdoors, (c) can be played at any season, (d) <u>is out of date,</u> (e) is outlawed in this country.

3 The best thing to do with a *mandate* is (a) eat it, (b) wear it, (c) throw it away, (d) <u>obey it,</u> (e) put it in the bank.

4 A *loquacious* person (a) sings well, (b) is silent, (c) <u>is talkative,</u> (d) travels a lot, (e) wears a uniform.

5 A person on a *pinnacle* (a) is on the bottom rung of a ladder, (b) <u>has gone about as high as possible,</u> (c) is living in a dream world, (d) sleeps on a featherbed, (e) is impatient because of the excitement.

6 The place for a *coronet* is (a) in the magazine rack, (b) in a jazz band, (c) in a cigar store, (d) on the dining-room table, (e) <u>on the head</u>.

7 If something is *negligible*, you might (a) take it to the cleaners, (b) <u>easily disregard it,</u> (c) shower it with attention, (d) invest it, (e) send it back to the factory.

8 A person of tremendous *girth* has (a) <u>a large waist measure,</u> (b) a lot of money, (c) great influence, (d) the intelligence of a genius, (e) an unlimited supply of energy.

9 A *coherent* person (a) <u>talks logically,</u> (b) can carry a tune, (c) babbles senselessly, (d) always seems in a hurry, (e) will eat anything.

10 A person who goes off on a *tangent* (a) takes a boat, (b) rides two on a bicycle, (c) <u>strays from the subject,</u> (d) gets angry, (e) goes on a fruit diet.

Circle each of the two words that are similar in meaning in each of the following groups. Underline the two words that are opposite in meaning.

EXAMPLE: (appetizing) approximate <u>bold</u> <u>modest</u> (tasty)

1 eminent <u>filthy</u> immaculate (imminent) (impending)

2 (appearance) crime openness (semblance) stealth

3 (economical) (frugal) prevalent scarce wild

4 (deadly) (fatal) cheerful injurious somber

5 acid alkaline (temporary) timely (transient)

6 figuratively <u>literally</u> literary (particularly) (specifically)

7 preventative precarious (precipitous) safe (steep)

8 (cumbersome) fast (heavy) mobile stationary

9 cheat (coquette) (flirt) master menial

10 (exotic) (foreign) prodigal runaway <u>thrifty</u>

Vocabulary Study/5

On the line at the left write the letter of the word or word group that means the same or nearly the same as the italicized word.

_d_ 1 *nettle* — (a) small patch, (b) trap for insects, (c) fine cord, (d) prickly plant, (e) young bird

_a_ 2 *chafe* — (a) make sore by rubbing, (b) poke fun at, (c) separate seeds from husks, (d) use a razor, (e) change course

_e_ 3 *aghast* — (a) disgusted, (b), eerie, (c) stern, (d) speechless, (e) horrified

_c_ 4 *mien* — (a) baseness, (b) one's self, (c) manner, (d) claim, (e) whim

_e_ 5 *fluctuation* — (a) overflowing, (b) healthy growth, (c) nervous confusion, (d) coming in of the tide, (e) changing back and forth

_b_ 6 *insinuate* — (a) do wrong, (b) hint, (c) insult, (d) falsify, (e) turn inside out

_b_ 7 *inter* — (a) go inside, (b) bury, (c) come between, (d) write, (e) rip

_d_ 8 *perennial* — (a) unmarried, (b) like a parent, (c) talkative, (d) lasting, (e) incidental

_c_ 9 *appraise* — (a) inform, (b) shower with compliments, (c) estimate the value of, (d) think something over, (e) move upward

_a_ 10 *saunter* — (a) stroll, (b) dampen, (c) wind around, (d) show off, (e) lag behind

_a_ 11 *vaunted* — (a) bragged about, (b) leaped over, (c) made useless, (d) jeered at, (e) overpriced

_d_ 12 *stratagem* — (a) semiprecious stone, (b) layer of rock, (c) measuring instrument, (d) trick, (e) court session

_c_ 13 *supersede* __ (a) leave off, (b) overpay, (c) replace, (d) go out of bounds, (e) snub

_b_ 14 *citadel* — (a) palace, (b) fortress, (c) wooded valley, (d) city dweller, (e) stringed instrument

_b_ 15 *zenith* — (a) radio wave, (b) high point, (c) garden flower, (d) metalworker, (e) old person

_d_ 16 *sunder* — (a) make a loud noise, (b) sell various small items, (c) become warm, (d) divide, (e) shock

_d_ 17 *disconcert* — (a) sing out of tune, (b) inconvenience, (c) put an end to, (d) confuse, (e) act independently.

_a_ 18 *guile* — (a) cunning deceit, (b) responsibility for a crime, (c) workers' union, (d) Dutch coin, (e) mask

_c_ 19 *remonstrate* — (a) explain again, (b) pay for services, (c) plead in protest, (d) bloom another season, (e) increase in size

_e_ 20 *potentate* — (a) honorary title, (b) conquered territory, (c) court decree, (d) druggist, (e) powerful ruler

_b_ 21 *protrude* — (a) trespass, (b) stick out, (c) draw out, (d) object to, (e) investigate

_e_ 22 *impunity* — (a) evil intention, (b) sincere conviction, (c) light-heartedness, (d) lack of modesty, (e) freedom from punishment

_a_ 23 *prate* — (a) talk foolishly, (b) plea prayerfully, (c) be sorry, (d) put off, (e) sob

_e_ 24 *deign* — (a) pretend, (b) prefer, (c) refuse, (d) tiptoe, (e) condescend

_c_ 25 *psyche* — (a) disease, (b) circle, (c) mind, (d) beautiful woman, (e) insane person

SCORE _____ (Top Score 25)

Vocabulary Study/6

At the left of the number write the letter of the word or phrase that is most nearly **opposite** in meaning to the italicized word.

__c__ 1 *balk* — (a) unwind, (b) stop, (c) continue, (d) jerk, (e) waste

__c__ 2 *hapless* __ (a) unfortunate, (b) capable, (c) lucky, (d) well-planned, (e) risky

__a__ 3 *inherent* — (a) apart from, (b) belonging to, (c) senseless, (d) not long enough, (e) not remembered in a will

__b__ 4 *privy* — (a) without a prayer, (b) known to all, (c) unofficial, (d) private, (e) of little importance

__e__ 5 *abashed* — (a) continuous, (b) unharmed, (c) blushing, (d) embarrassed, (e) self-confident

__d__ 6 *antagonism* — (a) forethought, (b) opposition,(c) weakness, (d) agreement, (e) hope

__b__ 7 *apprehensive* — (a) uneasy, (b) unafraid, (c) unwise, (d) free, (e) loud

__c__ 8 *depreciate* — (a) refuse to apologize, (b) make light of, (c) increase in value, (d) give back to, (e) do one's duty

__e__ 9 *dubious* — (a) doubtful, (b) good, (c) prejudiced, (d) guileless, (e) sure

__a__ 10 *infallible* — (a) liable to error, (b) without hesitation, (c) giving an incorrect impression, (d) held in low esteem, (e) always correct

__d__ 11 *copious* — (a) dry, (b) happy, (c) abundant, (d) scanty, (e) unduplicated

__e__ 12 *covert* — (a) secret, (b) greedy, (c) brace, (d) hopeful, (e) open

__b__ 13 *pallid* — (a) weak, (b) colorful, (c) alive, (d) upright, (e) inartistic

__e__ 14 *perturb* — (a) clean, (b) upset, (c) waken, (d) connect, (e) calm

__d__ 15 *momentous* — (a) far-reaching, (b) lasting, (c) inactive, (d) trivial, (e) immediate

__a__ 16 *inexorable* — (a) yielding, (b) undying, (c) prayerful, (d) airy, (e) relentless

__c__ 17 *chastise* — (a) taint, (b) become silent, (c) reward, (d) discipline, (e) lead

__b__ 18 *chronic* — (a) severe, (b) of short duration, (c) mild, (d) sudden, (e) cheerful

__a__ 19 *crude* — (a) elegant, (b) rough, (c) raw, (d) tasteless, (e) mature

__a__ 20 *impious* — (a) reverent, (b) ungodly, (c) sober, (d) slow, (e) graceful

__e__ 21 *encumber* — (a) heap together, (b) dislodge, (c) add to one's load, (d) attach no blame, (e) afford relief

__c__ 22 *languid* — (a) indifferent, (b) solid, (c) vigorous, (d) unattractive, (e) short

__d__ 23 *puny* — (a) without humor, (b) playful, (c) clean-smelling, (d) strong, (e) weak

__b__ 24 *feasible* — (a) undutiful, (b) impracticable, (c) hard, (d) possible, (e) sensible

__b__ 25 *belated* — (a) made glad, (b) early, (c) delayed, (d) lamented, (e) grumbled about

86

SCORE _____ (Top Score 25)

Vocabulary Study/7

The first two words form a pair. Find the word that makes a similar pair with the third word. Write the letter of this word at the left of the number.

EXAMPLE: _d_ wedding march : wedding : : dirge : (a) parade, (b) dance, (c) christening, (d) funeral, (e) battle

_c_ 1 smile : frown : : benediction : (a) worry, (b) prayer, (c) curse, (d) silence, (e) mumbling

_a_ 2 heat : thermostat : : fuel : (a) gas pedal, (b) steering wheel, (c) ignition, (d) carburetor, (e) brake

_c_ 3 nocturnal : night : : diurnal : (a) wakefulness, (b) moon, (c) day, (d) darkness, (e) light

_b_ 4 solar : sun : : lunar : (a) earth, (b) moon, (c) star, (d) planet, (e) satellite

_e_ 5 hitching post : horse : : quay : (a) automobile, (b) travel, (c) train, (d) pier, (e) ship

_d_ 6 wine : dregs : : river : (a) flood, (b) banks, (c) course, (d) sediment, (e) turbulence

_a_ 7 wholesome : health : : morbid : (a) disease, (b) food, (c) medicine, (d) mind, (e) psychology

_c_ 8 person : idle : : land : (a) sallow, (b) hallowed, (c) fallow, (d) callow, (e) shallow

_b_ 9 hot : cold : : volatile : (a) airy, (b) stable, (c) hazy, (d) underground, (e) cool

_e_ 10 spark : fire : : impetus : (a) fall, (b) ascent, (c) end, (d) argument, (e) motion

At the left write the letter of the word that best completes the sentence.

EXAMPLE: _b_ Much to my _____, I forgot the only line I was to speak and just had to stand there, red-faced. (a) surmise, (b) chagrin, (c) derision, (d) deportment, (e) retribution

_c_ 11 The operations officer thinks the fog will _____ before long and that we will take off on schedule. (a) disrupt, (b) dissent, (c) dissipate, (d) diverge, (e) distill

_b_ 12 He comes from a _____ family of middle-class, conventional shopkeepers. (a) Bohemian, (b) bourgeois, (c) socialistic, (d) productive, (e) proletarian

_a_ 13 It was a _____ crowd she addressed—people of all ages and all classes. (a) motley, (b) homogeneous, (c) illiterate, (d) disinterested, (e) spellbound

_c_ 14 Mr. Bly's decision will be a _____ one, because he is a wise and experienced person. (a) prejudiced, (b) tentative, (c) judicious, (d) peremptory, (e) patriotic

_e_ 15 Molly's description was so _____ that I felt as if I were seeing the sight myself. (a) grisly, (b) emotional, (c) vehement, (d) veritable, (e) graphic

_b_ 16 Howard is a _____ person, and I fear he will seek revenge. (a) deranged, (b) vindictive, (c) dumfounded, (d) zealous, (e) versatile

_a_ 17 The _____ stained-glass windows of the old cathedrals are lovely, but for the windows of our homes we want transparent glass. (a) translucent, (b) ornate, (c) luminous, (d) opaque, (e) expensive

_d_ 18 When the humidity is 100 percent, the air is _____ with water vapor. (a) sated, (b) distilled, (c) abounding, (d) saturated, (e) lavish

_a_ 19 You are no one's slave: you need not be _____ to anyone. (a) servile, (b) indebted, (c) obligated, (d) remorseful, (e) liable

_c_ 20 The singer always has a number of people hovering about him, like a prince with his _____. (a) delegation, (b) tribunal, (c) retinue, (d) menagerie, (e) auxiliary

SCORE _____ **(Top Score 20)**

Vocabulary Study/8

On the line at the left of the number, write the letter of the word or phrase that means the same or nearly the same as the italicized word. If there is no correct answer, write **X** on the line.

_c_ 1 *allocate* — (a) change location, (b) speak, (c) distribute, (d) approve, (e) unite

_e_ 2 *pallor* — (a) a dance, (b) a column, (c) an election, (d) a disease, (e) paleness

_e_ 3 *oblivious* — (a) restricted, (b) objectionable, (c) happy, (d) an angle, (e) forgetful

_a_ 4 *absurdity* — (a) that which is foolish, (b) that which is hateful, (c) that which is unsuccessful, (d) that which is profound, (e) that which is allowed

_b_ 5 *urban* — (a) country, (b) city, (c) sophisticated, (d) an acid, (e) study of stars

_e_ 6 *terrain* — (a) a turtle, (b) the sky, (c) the end, (d) a patio, (e) a tract of ground

_b_ 7 *blandishment* — (a) gentleness, (b) flattery, (c) a dessert, (d) imperfection, (e) fiction

_e_ 8 *butte* — (a) an animal, (b) an argument, (c) strike, (d) the end of a cigar, (e) a steep hill

_a_ 9 *legume* — (a) a vegetable, (b) a disease, (c) an insect, (d) a lawyer, (e) a body of soldiers

_a_ 10 *cascade* — (a) a steep waterfall, (b) a tree, (c) a wig, (d) a mountain, (e) a window

_c_ 11 *defunct* — (a) cheated, (b) challenge, (c) deceased, (d) degraded, (e) pay

_a_ 12 *skittish* — (a) extremely lively, (b) a small battle, (c) a short play, (d) sudden shower, (e) trickery

_d_ 13 *blasphemy* — (a) wonderful, (b) a skin disease, (c) a church official, (d) profanity, (e) indifference

_X_ 14 *arid* — (a) eager, (b) wet, (c) silly, (d) serious, (e) airy

_d_ 15 *banter* — (a) a large feast, (b) a diet, (c) a large flag, (d) good-natured ridiculing, (e) a stairway railing

_d_ 16 *stationary* — (a) sculpture, (b) growth, (c) law, (d) not moving, (e) writing paper

_b_ 17 *captivate* — (a) to take a prisoner, (b) fascinate, (c) to lead, (d) to capture a prize, (e) to overturn

_c_ 18 *alms* — (a) nuts, (b) fruits, (c) charitable gifts, (d) trees, (e) wealth

_e_ 19 *superfluous* — (a) magical, (b) the best, (c) miraculous, (d) expensive, (e) surplus

_e_ 20 *affront* — (a) gratify, (b) frighten, (c) trouble, (d) astray, (e) offend

_b_ 21 *chasm* — (a) a helmet, (b) a gorge, (c) a hunter, (d) a steep hill, (e) punishment

_X_ 22 *vehicle* — (a) furious, (b) a business enterprise, (c) a channel, (d) an opening, (e) a chamber of the heart

_e_ 23 *credulous* — (a) growing, (b) increase in sound, (c) climbing iron, (d) a sideboard, (e) inclined to believe

_e_ 24 *aversion* — (a) an escape, (b) greed, (c) an object of love, (d) the study of dirigibles, (e) dislike

_d_ 25 *archipelago* — (a) a mountain range, (b) mainland, (c) a church official, (d) a group of islands, (e) an archeologist

SCORE _____ (Top Score 25)

Vocabulary Study/9

The following sentences are taken from magazine articles. Read each sentence and try to figure out the meaning of the italicized word from the context. On the line provided, write what you think the word means. Check your answer in the dictionary.

1 Without the green of plants, the red-blooded animals of this earth could not exist, for virtually all forms of life draw their *sustenance* from green plants.

nourishment

2 The youngster showed a quick and engaging humor, a companionableness which at times *obliterated* the twenty years' difference in their ages.

blotted out, canceled

3 The other type of animal coloration due to physical structure is *iridescence*, just like that of oil films floating on water, or of soap bubbles.

a rainbowlike play of colors

4 It was a friendly meeting, and all concerned hoped that relations would be even more *amicable* in the future.

friendly

5 We have just completed a picture showing the trials and *tribulations* of an average letter carrier—all the obstacles that must be hurdled before the mail can finally be delivered to your door.

suffering, distresses

6 The progress of life is *devious*, traveling in erratic and surprising ways to reach unexpected ends.

winding

7 As their final number at the concert, the rock group sang a *medley* of their most popular songs.

a musical composition made up of a series of songs

8 Prior to the July, 1969 moon landing, many *simulated* flights to the moon were conducted by the Air Force.

pretended

9 Most early space exploration was conducted by *proxy*; robots were sent into space instead of human beings.

authority or power to act for another

10 The explorers of the past required courage, but astronauts who have ventured into space have been *intrepid* indeed.

fearless, bold

SCORE _____ (Top Score 10)

Vocabulary Study/10

In the following selection there are several words that may be unfamiliar to you. However there are good context clues to the meanings of most of the words. First read the selection through. Then match the italicized words with the definitions in the list below the selection. Write the number of the italicized word on the line before its definition. Use your dictionary whenever necessary.

If you want to know what it feels like to be ¹*flayed* alive, you should try being an extemporaneous speaker. Do you know what that is? You're given a topic and expected to deliver a ²*lucid* speech on it after a few minutes' preparation.

I was entered into an extemporaneous speech contest shortly after joining the ³*Forensic* League in school. My much admired, though ⁴*eccentric* English teacher admitted that I didn't have enough experience, but he thought it would be good for me. He said I had an ⁵*intrinsic* talent for that sort of thing. When I replied that I'd rather be in a Roman ⁶*amphitheater* facing fifty ⁷*predatory* lions, he answered ⁸*callously*, "Come, come, Tina. When I think how ⁹*glib* you were when you explained why you hadn't finished your term paper—"

"All right," I cried ¹⁰*petulantly*. "Blackmail, I believe, is the most ¹¹*despicable* crime."

So that's how I found myself among a group of ¹²*fanatically* well-prepared speech students. I was given a ¹³*prosaic* little topic—grain sales between the U.S. and the Soviet Union. My knowledge of the subject was ¹⁴*infinitesimal*, but I went forward with an ¹⁵*adamantine* spirit. I stood up and smiled ¹⁶*obsequiously* at the judges. I tried to look as if I were ¹⁷*deliriously* happy to make an ¹⁸*impromptu* speech on the subject. My face ¹⁹*emanated* pure joy. I began with a clever ²⁰*epigram*. Then I blushed—I didn't want to be too ²¹*ostentatious* about my vast knowledge. For five minutes, I sputtered some ²²*muddled* nonsense. My speech was—by forensic standards—²³*atrocious*. Believe me, it was not the ²⁴*apex* of my speaking career.

6 a	A circular building with tiered rows of seats surrounding an arena	20 m	A witty thought expressed in a few words
21 b	Inclined to show off	4 n	Odd
2 c	Easily understood	19 o	Sent out, as rays
11 d	Hateful	1 p	Skinned
13 e	Dull	10 q	Fretfully
5 f	Belonging to the very nature of a thing	18 r	Done without preparation
3 g	For studying the art of debating	23 s	Horrifying or barbaric
14 h	Extremely small	24 t	Highest point
8 i	In a hard-hearted way	12 u	With excessive enthusiasm
22 j	Confused	17 v	Insanely
9 k	Said easily and smoothly	15 w	Not to be broken
16 l	In a cringingly obedient way	7 x	Tending to prey on other animals

90

Vocabulary Study/11

If you learn just a few Latin words, you can learn hundreds of English words built from these words. In this lesson ten Latin roots are given. (A root is the base or stem of a word.) The meaning of each root is given. Then two English words built from the root are given with their meanings. Then two more derived words are listed. Write the meaning of each of these words. If you are not sure of a meaning, use your dictionary.

1 **aqua** meaning "water"
aqualung — device for breathing under water
aquarium a tank of water for keeping fish or plants

aqueous — watery
aqueduct a channel for flowing water

2 **corp, corpor** meaning "body"
corporal — of the human body, physical
corporate formed into a body by legal enactment

corpuscle — tiny body forming part of the blood
corpulent very fat

3 **domin** meaning "master," "lord"
domain — territory over which one is master

dominate to rule

dominion — supreme authority; sovereign power; absolute ownership
domineer to rule with insolence

4 **mort** meaning "death"
mortal — liable to death
mortally fatally; deadly

mortification — humiliation
mortician an undertaker

5 **multi** meaning "many," "much"
multiply — increase in number

multiple containing more than one

multigraph — machine for copying typewritten material
multimillionaire one having millions of dollars

6 **omni** meaning "all"
omnibus — bus that carries many people
omnipresent present everywhere at once

omnipotent — all powerful
omnivorous eating everything; both animal and vegetable

7 **ped** meaning "foot"
centipede — small, wormlike animal with many pairs of legs
impede obstruct; hinder

pedestrian — a foot traveler

velocipede a light vehicle propelled by the feet

8 **prim** meaning "first"
prime — of first importance or quality
primary first in order, time, or development

primitive — first or early in development
primate one who is first in rank or authority

9 **soci** meaning "companion"
social — pertaining to companionship

sociable friendly, companionable

socialism — system of social organization based on collective ownership
sociology the science of the origin and evolution of society

10 **sol** meaning "alone"
sole — being the only one
soliloquy act of talking to oneself

solitude — state of being alone
solitaire a game that one person can play alone

91

Vocabulary Study/12

One meaning of **pro** is "for," and one meaning of **con** is "against." The prefix **pro** can mean "before," "for," "in front," "forth," "in behalf of," "in place of," "according to." The prefix **con** can mean "with," "together," "very." Add the needed letters to make ten **pro** words and ten **con** words. Each blank indicates a letter. The definition follows the blanks. A possible use of the word is indicated in the parentheses.

1 Pro f a n e not sacred (_____ literature)

2 Pro f e s s declare, admit freely (to _____ ignorance)

3 Pro f f e r offer for acceptance (to _____ assistance)

4 Pro f i c i e n t expert, skilled (a _____ typist)

5 Pro f i l e side view of the face (not a fullface, but a _____ view)

6 Pro f o u n d deep, intense (a _____ thinker, like Einstein)

7 Pro g e n y offspring (not only for our generation but for our _____)

8 Pro h i b i t forbid (laws that _____ gambling)

9 Pro l o g u e preface, introduction (the _____ to a play)

10 Pro s p e c t i v e expected, hoped for (a _____ customer)

1 Con c e i t e d having a high opinion of oneself (so _____ that one thinks one can do anything)

2 Con c e p t thought, general idea (Galileo changed our _____ of the solar system.)

3 Con c e s s i o n that which is yielded (Both sides made a _____ and the treaty was signed.)

4 Con c i s e condensed, short (a clear, _____ statement)

5 Con g e s t e d blocked, overcrowded (_____ traffic)

6 Con j e c t u r e a guess (only a _____, unsupported by evidence)

7 Con j u r e to summon a devil or spirit (to _____ a genie, as Aladdin did)

8 Con s e c r a t e to make sacred ("We cannot _____, we cannot hallow this ground.")

9 Con s e c u t i v e in order, one after the other (It rained on four _____ days.)

10 Con t a g i o u s catching (a _____ disease, like whopping cough)

SCORE _____ (Top Score 20)

Vocabulary Study/13

An error like "Two people can ride on a tantrum" is called a "boner." A something-like-it word is used for the right word: *tantrum* for *tandem*. In each sentence, cross out the word that is incorrectly used. Write the correct word at the end of the sentence. Be able to give the meaning of both words.

1 The convention would be open to any state declared ~~edible~~ by the United Nations. _____eligible_____

2 The President discarded most of the prepared talk and spoke ~~extraneously~~ from notes. _____extemporaneously_____

3 She has a modest, almost ~~self-defacing~~ manner. _____self-effacing_____

4 The ~~insurgent~~ in the patient's side was five inches long. _____incision_____

5 The flood reports did not tell the extent of the ~~travesty~~. _____tragedy_____

6 Jane has a real genius for acting; according to her teacher, all she needs is a course in <u>electrocution</u> to finish her off properly. _____elocution_____

7 The president then introduced Mr. Meeker, who, in his own ~~inimical~~ fashion, served as toastmaster for the evening. _____inimitable_____

8 If you are ~~decapitated~~ due to illness, your salary will be mailed to you. _____incapacitated_____

9 Mother thinks I need new glasses, and so she made an appointment for me at the <u>optimist's</u>. _____optometrist's_____

10 Gibraltar is considered an ~~invisible~~ fortress. _____invincible_____

What is the best, or most practical, thing to do with each of these? At the left, write the letter of the answer that most clearly illustrates the meaning of the italicized word.

b 1 *an anemone?* — (a) put it in the soup, (b) pick it in the woods, (c) ask him his real name, (d) put it back in the cupboard.

a 2 *a piazza?* — (a) sit out on it, (b) eat it at an Italian restaurant, (c) play a tune on it, (d) exchange it for American money.

d 3 *a jerkin?* — (a) put it in a relish, (b) train it to wait quietly, (c) tie up a boat at it, (d) wear it.

a 4 *a malady?* — (a) try to cure it, (b) admire her costume, (c) try to put him at his ease, (d) put him in jail.

c 5 *a diadem?* — (a) lecture from it, (b) wear it on your finger, (c) put it on your head, (d) deposit it in the bank.

c 6 *a bolster?* — (a) strain vegetables with it, (b) put a gun in it, (c) put it on the bed, (d) pick cotton with it.

d 7 *a valise?* — (a) dance it, (b) swallow it, (c) answer it, (d) pack clothes in it.

b 8 *a vendor?* — (a) open it for more air, (b) buy something from him, (c) scrape it off to see what is underneath, (d) grant him the respect due the aged.

b 9 *a paddock?* — (a) throw a harpoon at it, (b) put your horse into it, (c) grow rice in it, (d) use it to get your boat moving.

c 10 *an auger?* — (a) get over it in time, (b) run away from it as fast as you can, (c) bore holes with it, (d) tell him you don't believe in fortune-telling.

93

SCORE _____ (Top Score 20)

Vocabulary Study/14

On the line at the left write the letter of the word or word group that means the same or nearly the same as the italicized word.

b 1 *apparition* — (a) complicated machinery, (b) ghostly appearance, (c) soothing application, (d) on-the-job training, (e) room divider

d 2 *entrepreneur* — (a) slave driver, (b) intimate friend, (c) will-o'-the-wisp, (d) business venturer, (e) talkative person

e 3 *impeach* — (a) remove from office, (b) deliver a sermon, (c) put a curse on, (d) behave virtuously, (e) accuse of misconduct in office

b 4 *labyrinth* — (a) workshop, (b) maze, (c) place for bathing, (d) cluster of trees, (e) jeweled necklace

a 5 *pillage* — (a) plunder, (b) dose of medicine, (c) cushion materials, (d) series of columns, (e) ridicule

e 6 *promontory* — (a) promise to pay, (b) public walk, (c) forward push, (d) quick action, (e) headland

d 7 *broach* — (a) close a gap, (b) ask a favor, (c) cook over a flame, (d) mention, (e) trespass

a 8 *engender* — (a) produce, (b) classify by sex, (c) indicate possession, (d) deduce, (e) deny entrance

a 9 *engross* — (a) occupy fully, (b) behave very badly, (c) eat too much, (d) enter a complaint, (e) break into parts

e 10 *rendezvous* — (a) hotel, (b) emotional disturbance, (c) relinquishment, (d) short poem, (e) meeting place

b 11 *salvage* — (a) soothe, (b) save from loss, (c) offer on a platter, (d) rob, (e) add seasoning

d 12 *abstinence* — (a) stubbornness, (b) insulting behavior, (c) righteousness, (d) forbearance, (e) nonconformity

c 13 *acrid* — (a) dry, (b) covering a considerable territory, (c) sharp to the taste, (d) bright, (e) energetic

c 14 *alienate* — (a) sue, (b) deport, (c) estrange, (d) make sick, (e) appease

a 15 *carrion* — (a) dead and rotting flesh, (b) soldiers, (c) clear and shrill call, (d) heavy-duty truck, (e) noisy party

e 16 *harangue* — (a) large ape, (b) closed carriage, (c) delaying action, (d) pattern of slanting lines, (e) ranting speech

d 17 *ferret* — (a) put chains on, (b) carry across a river, (c) deck out, (d) draw out of hiding, (e) grumble

d 18 *conciliate* — (a) add to a will, (b) systematize, (c) hurry, (d) pacify, (e) bring to an end

b 19 *auspicious* — (a) overbearing, (b) favorable, (c) stern, (d) majestic, (e) overweight

e 20 *capitulate* — (a) cut off the head, (b) make fun of, (c) hurl, (d) change one's mind, (e) surrender

SCORE _____ **(Top Score 20)**

Vocabulary Study/15

At the left of the number write the letter of the word or phrase that is most nearly **opposite** in meaning to the italicized word.

_b_ 1 *abomination* — (a) continuation, (b) liking, (c) digestion, (d) aversion, (e) success

_e_ 2 *bountiful* — (a) pertaining to the land, (b) generous, (c) determined, (d) unlimited, (e) stingy

_e_ 3 *coy* — (a) reserved, (b) masculine, (c) afraid, (d) intelligent, (e) bold

_c_ 4 *debase* — (a) cure, (b) begin, (c) raise, (d) make fun of, (e) reduce in value

_c_ 5 *demure* — (a) impolite, (b) uncomplaining, (c) immodest, (d) inhibited, (e) out of proportion

_a_ 6 *diffidence* — (a) confidence, (b) shyness, (c) concern, (d) similarity, (e) compactness

_a_ 7 *disconsolate* — (a) happy, (b) unified, (c) comfortless, (d) harmonious, (e) steady

_d_ 8 *disheveled* — (a) stored away, (b) clean, (c) encouraged, (d) tidy, (e) ruffled

_d_ 9 *doff* — (a) greet, (b) trail behind, (c) remain firm, (d) put on, (e) be caught

_e_ 10 *dormant* — (a) spineless, (b) untamed, (c) flexible, (d) sleeping, (e) active

_c_ 11 *elation* — (a) promptness, (b) high spirits, (c) despair, (d) apparentness, (e) stillness

_d_ 12 *embellished* — (a) adorned, (b) thin, (c) poised, (d) plain, (e) stolen

_c_ 13 *extricate* — (a) admit, (b) destroy, (c) entangle, (d) overestimate, (e) free

_a_ 14 *fealty* — (a) disloyalty, (b) intangible property, (c) insensitivity, (d) lack of skill, (e) obligation

_d_ 15 *fictitious* — (a) untruthful, (b) imaginary, (c) literary, (d) genuine, (e) constant

_e_ 16 *finesse* — (a) delicacy, (b) cheapness, (c) strength, (d) inattention, (e) clumsiness

_c_ 17 *flippant* — (a) permanent, (b) strong, (c) respectful, (d) happy, (e) unsteady

_b_ 18 *gainsay* — (a) repeat, (b) affirm, (c) give up, (d) misdirect, (e) deny

_b_ 19 *inanimate* — (a) faraway, (b) alive, (c) hard, (d) lifeless, (e) yielding

_e_ 20 *indigenous* — (a) wealthy, (b) wandering, (c) natural, (d) pleased, (e) foreign

_a_ 21 *indulgent* — (a) strict, (b) humoring, (c) skinny, (d) overweight, (e) sober

_e_ 22 *innate* — (a) casual, (b) guilty, (c) native, (d) nervous, (e) acquired

_b_ 23 *malign* — (a) pretend, (b) flatter, (c) heal, (d) succeed, (e) slander

_b_ 24 *mitigate* — (a) purify, (b) aggravate, (c) lessen, (d) settle out of court, (c) cease fighting

_d_ 25 *morose* — (a) sullen, (b) alert, (c) sleepy, (d) cheerful, (e) stupid

SCORE _____ (Top Score 25)

Vocabulary Study/16

The first two words form a pair. Find the word that makes a similar pair with the third word. Write the letter of this word at the left.

EXAMPLE: _d_ hatband : hat : : frieze : (a) dress, (b) equator, (c) cake, (d) wall

_d_ 1 busy : bee : : wily : (a) lion, (b) goose, (c) tiger, (d) fox

_b_ 2 broccoli : vegetable : : brocade : (a) book, (b) fabric, (c) vehicle, (d) shoe

_a_ 3 ducks : decoy : : mice : (a) cheese, (b) rodent, (c) family, (d) quietness

_d_ 4 chair : sitting : : pallet : (a) riding, (b) drinking, (c) sailing, (d) sleeping

_a_ 5 pecuniary : money : : culinary : (a) kitchen, (b) leather, (c) farm, (d) color

_c_ 6 spouse : marriage : : accomplice : (a) partner,(b) divorce, (c) crime, (d) war

_b_ 7 censer : incense : : fireplace : (a) bricks, (b) wood, (c) snake, (d) hearth

_c_ 8 hypocritical : sincere : : inarticulate : (a) skillful, (b) artistic, (c) distinct, (d) unintelligible

_d_ 9 tepid : hot : : cool : (a) warm, (b) snowy, (c) blustery, (d) frigid

_b_ 10 zephyr : gale : : sprinkle : (a) thunder, (b) downpour, (c) earthquake, (d) umbrella

At the left write the letter of the word that best completes the sentence.

EXAMPLE: _b_ If sewage from the factories is dumped into the river, it will _____ the water. (a) mutilate, (b) contaminate, (c) endue, (d) imbue, (e) pilfer

_e_ 1 It was later found that an error had been made in the certification, and so the marriage was _____. (a) pronounced, (b) amassed, (c) accelerated, (d) retrieved, (e) annulled

_d_ 2 The artist grew up on a ranch, and he carries out the Western _____ in all his designs. (a) fanaticism, (b) aesthetic, (c) flavor, (d) motif, (e) spirit

_d_ 3 The speaker _____ his statement by giving examples and illustrations. (a) distended, (b) precluded, (c) incited, (d) amplified, (e) evoked

_a_ 4 Since Lois is so good at _____, we'll ask her to draw the cartoons for the "School Personalities" page. (a) caricature, (b) deposition, (c) characterization, (d) intuition, (e) parable

_e_ 5 Linda is a vibrant, exciting individual, and Bob is completely _____ of her. (a) sated, (b) deluded, (c) cowered, (d) amalgamated, (e) enamored

_c_ 6 The warships of a country at war may seize and destroy _____ goods which are being shipped to its enemy in neutral ships. (a) flagrant, (b) mercantile, (c) contraband, (d) obnoxious, (e) poisonous

_b_ 7 Woodchucks, frogs, and snakes _____ during cold weather and hence need no food in the winter. (a) encroach, (b) hibernate, (c) efface, (d) transpire, (e) migrate

_b_ 8 The Better Business Bureau was organized to protect the public from unfair, misleading, and _____ advertising and business methods. (a) facetious, (b) fraudulent, (c) callous, (d) implacable, (e) ungainly

_d_ 9 All day long it was talk, talk, talk; I had never before met such a _____ person. (a) voluptuous, (b) vociferous, (c) vivacious, (d) voluble, (e) visionary

_a_ 10 The rest of us grew tired and stopped, but John was seemingly _____ and kept on and on. (a) indefatigable, (b) versatile, (c) tenacious, (d) agile, (e) conversant

SCORE _____ (Top Score 20)

Vocabulary Study/17

Here are some common Greek combining forms and their meanings. Each one is numbered. Add the forms, according to the directions, to make good English words. On the line following each "equation," write the English word formed and a short definition of the word.

1 **anthropo** — human being
2 **arch** — ruler
3 **auto** — self
4 **bio** — life
5 **geo** — earth
6 **graph, graphy** — writing
7 **litho, lith** stone

8 **logy** — science of
9 **mega** — large
10 **meter, metry** —measure
11 **micro** — small
12 **mon, mono** — one
13 **patho, path** — suffering
14 **phone** — sound

15 **photo** — light
16 **psycho** — mind
17 **scope** — means for seeing
18 **stat** — apparatus for holding stationary
19 **tele** — far, far away
20 **thermo** — heat

EXAMPLE: 4 + 8 = _biology—the science of life_

1 + 8 = anthropology—the science of human beings

12 + 2 = monarch — one ruler

3 + 6 = autograph — a person's own writing

4 + 6 = biography — the written history of a person's life

5 + 8 = geology — the science of the earth

19 + 6 = telegraph — a system for communication at a distance

7 + 6 = lithograph — a print made from a specially prepared stone

13 + 8 = pathology — the science dealing with disease

9 + 14 = megaphone — a device to magnify sound

11 + 10 = micrometer — an instrument for measuring minute distances

11 + 17 = microscope — an instrument for inspecting objects too small to be seen

12 + 7 = monolith — a statue formed of a single block of stone

16 + 13 = psychopath — one suffering from mental disease

11 + 14 = microphone — an instrument for intensifying feeble sounds

15 + 10 = photometer — an instrument for measuring the intensity of light

16 + 8 = psychology — the science dealing with the mind

19 + 17 = telescope — an instrument for making distant objects appear larger and nearer

20 + 18 = thermostat — apparatus for holding heat stationary

19 + 15 = telephoto — pertaining to a photographic lens which produces larger images from a given distance

20 + 10 = thermometer — an instrument for measuring heat

SCORE _____ (Top Score 20)

97

Vocabulary Study/18

Some words that seem to resemble each other often have completely different meanings. A superficial resemblance between words may cause a person to refer to someone as "the curio of the museum" (*curio* for *curator*). A person who knows the meaning of the words he uses will not make such "boners."

In each of the following sentences cross out the "boner." After the sentence write the word, and the meaning of the word, that should have been used.

1 The forecast says "Northwest winds diminishing a little and rather high ~~humanity~~."
   humidity — moisture; dampness, especially of the atmosphere

2 ~~Misinformed~~ shellfish are most likely to grow pearls.
   misformed (*or* malformed) — abnormally formed

3 The Bureau of Standards insures the use of ~~uninformed~~ weights and measures.
   uniform — having always the same form, manner, or degree

4 The dinner will be held in the Oak Room, and the lecture will be given in the ~~adjourning~~ room.
   adjoining — meeting or touching at some point or line; adjacent

5 Fortunately, we were able to administer the ~~anecdote~~ and revive them.
   antidote — remedy to counteract the effects of poison

6 Anne had an ~~airy~~ feeling as she peered in the window of the haunted house.
   eerie — strange, mysterious, weird

7 Most diseases are not inherited; a few are ~~congenial~~.
   congenital — existing at, or dating from, birth

8 The judge declared that the testimony was ~~irreverent~~ to the facts.
   irrelevant — not applicable or pertinent

9 It is rumored that the neglected and ~~dilated~~ house down the street is haunted.
   dilapidated — fallen into ruin or decay

10 These people were very wealthy; they were business ~~typhoons~~.
   tycoons-business people of great wealth and power

11 The two parts of an egg are the albumen and the ~~yoke~~.
   yolk — the yellow of an egg

12 It's just a small gift, but it will serve as a ~~memorandum~~ of your visit.
   memento — something to awaken memory

13 Another name for a funeral parlor is a ~~moratorium~~.
   mortuary — a place where dead bodies are kept for a time before burial

14 The inscription on a tomb is called an ~~epithet~~.
   epitaph — an inscription on or at a tomb in memory of the one buried there

15 We get our water from ~~artisan~~ wells.
   artesian — a deep bored well (water flows up like a fountain)

98

Vocabulary Study/19

The following sentences are taken from magazine articles. Read each sentence and try to figure out the meaning of the italicized word from the context. On the line provided, write what you think the word means. Check your answer with the dictionary.

1 The typhoon-*wracked* China Coast is a rough spot at any time.

   ruined

2 An unbelievably *oppressive* blanket of humidity lies over the area, and perspiration clings to the suffocating skin like acid.

   overpowering

3 On nights when the foghorn bellows and the surf thunders on the rocks, the lighthouse keepers sleep *fitfully*.

   restlessly

4 Mr. Busch admitted frankly that he had never been an ardent *devotee* of the national pastime of baseball.

   enthusiast

5 I'm fairly *fluent*, and usually I have no trouble starting a conversation.

   ready in the use of words

6 In dry spells cowhands, using special blowtorches, *singe* the prickly pears to remove their spines, and the juicy leaves make good roughage for cattle.

   remove by burning

7 You can't blame the President for a drought; it's silly to try to make him the *scapegoat* of the disaster.

   person bearing the blame

8 The Romans adored oysters; Vitellius, a notoriously *gluttonous* emperor, is credited with having consumed more oysters at a single sitting than any other man—well over a thousand.

   one who eats excessively

9 As a result of her *festering* wound, Caroline was advised by her doctors to remain at University Hospital an extra two weeks.

   inflamed; generating pus

10 In this desert the hollows between the mesquite-covered *hummocks* are sprinkled with fragments of brilliantly painted pottery.

   small rounded hills

11 Contrary to *fallacious* public opinion, a jet engine does not push against the air to gain its impetus.

   faulty

12 Oysters are the most *sedentary* creatures imaginable; having no means of locomotion, they attach themselves in infancy to whatever hard surface they happen to settle on.

   settled; not migrating

13 For some reason, many people refuse to taste catfish, but I think it's one of the most *succulent* of table fish.

   juicy and tasty

14 On game nights the gymnasium is a complete *bedlam* with a brass band trying to break out the walls and a few hundred shrill voices added to the din.

   madhouse

99

Vocabulary Study/20

This vocabulary lesson is devoted to words pertaining to business. New and young employees cannot be expected to have the specialized knowledge that experienced people have, but they should have a general knowledge of commonly used business terms.

After reading each sentence, underline the words or phrases which most nearly fit the meaning of the italicized words as used in the sentence. You may need to refer to the dictionary.

EXAMPLE: Since he had sufficient collateral, you will be reimbursed for the loan.

collateral — business sense, side interest, property offered as security, money in the bank

reimbursed — pleased, repaid, granted an interview, notified

1 Ms. Olin requires her salespeople to render a strict accounting of all their expenditures.

accounting — savings, alibi, record, complaint

expenditures — extravagances, spending, investments, losses

2 If we are to avoid bankruptcy, we must obtain capital to finance our operations until we can fill our backlog.

bankruptcy — holding up a bank, insolvency, interruption of business, loss of prestige

capital — influence, money, punishment, debts

finance — pay for, liquidate, ship, sell

operations — surgery, military actions, work, gambling

backlog — bank account, unfilled orders, deficit, warehouse

3 The union, which is an affiliate of the American Federation of Labor, is negotiating with the management of Glee & Co., a subsidiary of Thornton, Inc.

100

union — the United States, radicals, consolidation, labor organization

affiliate — associate, enemy, competitor, supporter

negotiating — bickering, cheating, seeking to come to terms, getting angry

management — competitor, executives, subordinates, foremen

subsidiary — submarine manufacturer, successor, firm controlled by another, dairy concern

Inc. — legal corporation, ink factory, incapacitated or bankrupt firm, bank

4 The accrued interest on your debentures now exceeds the principal.

accrued — accumulated, forfeited, compound, simple

interest — excitement, debt, right, capital earnings

debentures — certificates of indebtedness, bills, bent products, factories

principal — school official, profit, capital sum, loss

5 The corporation's franchise expires at the end of this fiscal year.

corporation — farmers' cooperative, factory, retail store, group recognized as a legal entity

franchise — permit to trade with France, permit to do business, right to vote, right to send letters without postage

fiscal — current, favorable, September 1 to August 31, pertaining to the period for which accounts are balanced

SCORE _____ (Top Score 20)

Vocabulary Study/21

This vocabulary lesson and Vocabulary Study 22 are modeled upon the verbal-aptitude sections of college-entrance examinations. Each of the lessons is different, for different types of questions appear in college-entrance examinations. Be sure to read the directions carefully.

On the line at the left of the number, write the letter of the word or word group that means the same or nearly the same as the italicized word.

__e__ 1 *denizen* — (a) evil spirit, (b) fish, (c) traveler, (d) society woman, (e) inhabitant

__e__ 2 *suppliant* — (a) diner, (b) addition, (c) dancer, (d) theory, (e) petitioner

__d__ 3 *tenure* — (a) suspense, (b) decade, (c) experiment, (d) holding, (e) force

__d__ 4 *longevity* — (a) foresight, (b) great distance, (c) practical joke, (d) length of life, (e) patience

__a__ 5 *incumbent* — (a) obligatory, (b) newly arrived, (c) out of shape, (d) poor, (e) ineffectual

__c__ 6 *ruminate* — (a) search, (b) vomit, (c) ponder, (d) dream, (e) wander

__b__ 7 *reticent* — (a) late, (b) silent, (c) held back, (d) following, (e) well-behaved

__c__ 8 *rampant* — (a) excited, (b) irritated, (c) unrestrained, (d) haphazard, (e) protected

__a__ 9 *vagary* — (a) caprice, (b) indefiniteness, (c) beggar, (d) excessive pride, (e) emptiness

__d__ 10 *acme* — (a) skin condition, (b) envy, (c) center, (d) highest point, (e) prized possession

__e__ 11 *stoic* — (a) heroic, (b) unfathomable, (c) stupid, (d) thick, (e) impassive

__c__ 12 *parley* — (a) bet, (b) front room, (c) conference, (d) standard, (e) barrage

__b__ 13 *subjugate* — (a) join, (b) conquer, (c) judge, (d) elevate, (e) expose

__b__ 14 *verity* — (a) change, (b) truth, (c) eternity, (d) short poem, (e) unusual excellence

__e__ 15 *presage* — (a) publish, (b) apply pressure, (c) make ready, (d) keep safe, (e) portend

__b__ 16 *obviate* — (a) atone for, (b) make unnecessary, (c) die, (d) invalidate, (e) forget

__e__ 17 *elicit* — (a) break a law, (b) escape, (c) omit, (d) give permission, (e) draw out

__d__ 18 *enigma* — (a) itching, (b) fatigue, (c) boredom, (d) puzzle, (e) beauty

__a__ 19 *abrogate* — (a) annul, (b) introduce, (c) irritate, (d) forgive, (e) condense

__a__ 20 *condone* — (a) pardon, (b) sympathize, (c) entrust, (d) disapprove, (e) argue

__c__ 21 *criterion* — (a) estimate, (b) illegal agreement, (c) standard, (d) religious principle, (e) sampling

__c__ 22 *florid* — (a) intoxicated, (b) strange, (c) high-colored, (d) tropical, (e) ill

__b__ 23 *foible* — (a) ornament, (b) failing, (c) trick, (d) sin, (e) burden

__a__ 24 *ebullient* — (a) bubbly, (b) receding, (c) stubborn, (d) wealthy, (e) threatening

__a__ 25 *cursory* — (a) superficial, (b) matter-of-fact, (c) thorough, (d) censorious, (e) out-of-the-way

SCORE _____ (Top Score 25)

Vocabulary Study/22

On the line at the left of the number, write the letter of the word that is most nearly opposite in meaning to the italicized word.

c __ 1 *convene* — (a) meet, (b) hamper, (c) disband, (d) release, (e) accommodate

e __ 2 *diffusion* — (a) dimness, (b) dispersal, (c) similarity, (d) order, (e) concentration

d __ 3 *dolorous* — (a) poor, (b) wide-awake, (c) anguished, (d) joyful, (e) masculine

b __ 4 *emaciated* — (a) unemotional, (b) fat, (c) unsympathetic, (d) fleshless, (e) fragrant

e __ 5 *fusion* — (a) coalescence, (b) bombardment, (c) carelessness, (d) vagueness, (e) separation

b __ 6 *spurious* — (a) impulsive, (b) genuine, (c) false, (d) thoughtful, (e) complimentary

d __ 7 *jeopardy* — (a) trust, (b) vulnerability, (c) reprieve, (d) safety, (e) victory

c __ 8 *reprimand* — (a) payment, (b) attraction, (c) commendation, (d) reproof, (e) self-esteem

a __ 9 *proximity* — (a) remoteness, (b) absence, (c) repulsion, (d) extravagance, (e) nearness

d __ 10 *perfunctory* — (a) indifferent, (b) fresh, (c) unofficial, (d) zealous, (e) servile

c __ 11 *pretentious* — (a) real, (b) showy, (c) modest, (d) imaginary, (e) portentous

d __ 12 *satiate* — (a) please, (b) lighten, (c) surfeit (d) starve, (e) dehydrate

a __ 13 *unwonted* — (a) customary, (b) desired, (c) heralded, (d) deserved, (e) unexpected

a __ 14 *vacillation* — (a) steadiness, (b) occupation, (c) shamelessness, (d) hesitation, (e) health

e __ 15 *penury* — (a) stinginess, (b) affability, (c) employment, (d) thoughtfulness, (e) opulence

c __ 16 *abortive* — (a) exact, (b) fruitless, (c) successful, (d) deterring, (e) enjoyable

e __ 17 *contrite* — (a) unforgiving, (b) ingenuous, (c) sorry, (d) flattering, (e) impenitent

c __ 18 *alleviate* — (a) make sad, (b) unite, (c) aggravate, (d) raise, (e) relieve

a __ 19 *altruistic* — (a) selfish, (b) untrustworthy, (c) incompetent, (d) egoistic, (e) unchanged

e __ 20 *egress* — (a) emergence, (b) fame, (c) baldness, (d) shield, (e) entrance

b __ 21 *ameliorate* — (a) sweeten, (b) worsen, (c) improve, (d) resist change, (e) forget

b __ 22 *innocuous* — (a) consequential, (b) harmful, (c) vaccinated, (d) guilty, (e) noninjurious

b __ 23 *astute* — (a) crooked, (b) stupid, (c) thin, (d) sagacious, (e) full-grown

d __ 24 *clemency* — (a) depression, (b) mercy, (c) difficulty, (d) harshness, (e) cheerfulness

a __ 25 *ephemeral* — (a) long-lived, (b) grave, (c) rugged, (d) bony, (e) fleeting

102

SCORE _____ (Top Score 25)

I. *Sentence Sense*   15 Points

On the line preceding each group of words, write **0** if the group is not a complete sentence; write **1** if the group is one complete sentence; or write **2** if the group is two sentences incorrectly written as one.

EXAMPLE: _0_ A wonderful place for a picnic.

_1_ 1 Bring your camera with you when you come to see me.

_0_ 2 When all the arrangements were made for a celebration.

_0_ 3 Wandering along a lonely country road in the hot sun.

_2_ 4 Enrique is the most energetic student in our class, he never seems to be tired.

_0_ 5 Saw a wonderful television program last Sunday.

_1_ 6 Striving always to do good work, Donna reached her goal.

_2_ 7 Reading is pleasant entertainment what kind of reading do you like?

_0_ 8 After the excitement of the day was finally over.

_2_ 9 Bob Weldon is class president all the members respect him greatly.

_0_ 10 A beautiful valley surrounded by rugged mountains.

_2_ 11 It was the most exciting game of the season we won by two points.

_0_ 12 Just the kind of afternoon for a tennis match.

_1_ 13 The principal and the teachers called the meeting and made the plans.

_0_ 14 While Helen and I waited for the other golfers.

_0_ 15 Because he was always impatient with other people.

Plain English Handbook, 1–4, 33–37.

II. *Essential Parts of the Sentence*   20 Points

For each sentence, write the simple subject on the first line and the simple predicate on the second line.

EXAMPLE: ___Longfellow___ ___Was born___ Was Longfellow born in Maine?

___constitution___ ___has been written___ 1 Has our club constitution been written?

___sunshine___ ___came___ 2 After days of rain came the sunshine.

___dog___ ___had been waiting___ 3 The dog, expecting its master, had been waiting a long time.

103

Marcella	Has returned	4 Has Marcella returned from Boston?
cloud	floated	5 Above the highest peak floated a big cloud.
dog	did see	6 Sleeping quietly, the dog did not see us.
flowers	were blooming	7 Around the mill were blooming many flowers.
Joe	Was	8 Was Joe, our club chairperson, at the game?
boys	Have been walking	9 Have the boys been walking to school?
Ed	rode	10 Behind the parade rode Ed on a big horse.

Plain English Handbook, 3, 4, 13, 15.

III. *Combining Groups of Words*   65 Points

Make one complete sentence of the two groups of words in each item by indicating the punctuation and capitalization needed at each point marked by a number in parentheses. Tell the part of speech of the italicized words. On the first line (marked 1) before each item give the class of the reconstructed sentence. Use the following key:

S — simple	**a** — comma	**d** — no punctuation	**g** — pronoun	**j** — adverb
Cd — compound	**b** — semicolon	**e** — small letter	**h** — verb	**k** — adjective
Cx — complex	**c** — colon	**f** — conjunction	**i** — noun	**l** — preposition

EXAMPLE: 1 *S* 2 *a* 3 *e* 4 *k*   We enjoyed the show (2) (3)Especially the (4)*musical* numbers.

1 Cx 2 d 3 e 4 h   1 Juan cannot win the contest (2) (3)Unless he (4)*works* harder.

1 Cd 2 b 3 e 4 h 5 k   2 Al is always courteous (2) (3)He (4)is a (5)*thoughtful* person.

1 Cd 2 i 3 b 4 e   3 Alice is (2)*chairperson* of the group (3) (4)She is a sophomore.

1 Cd 2 j 3 b 4 e 5 i   4 Jo is (2)*extremely* ambitious (3) (4)She always uses good (5)*language*.

1 Cd 2 i 3 a 4 e   5 Ted dreams of a great (2)*future* (3) (4)But dreams cannot bring success.

1 Cx 2 a 3 e 4 k 5 i   6 Before the others came (2) (3)He and I had (4)*the* (5)*work* done.

1 Cd 2 a 3 e 4 h   7 Success requires work (2) (3)But some people (4)*shun* hard work.

1 Cd 2 h 3 b 4 f 5 g   8 Dot and Stu (2)*wrote* the stories (3) Liz (4)*and* (5)I edited them.

1 Cx 2 d 3 e 4 g   9 Maria wrote her story (2) (3)Before (4)*she* came to school.

1 Cd 2 b 3 e 4 j   10 Jack is very careless (2) (3)He will (4)*never* finish in time.

1 S 2 a 3 e 4 i   11 Many people enjoy sports (2) (3)Particularly (4)*football*.

1 S 2 a 3 e 4 i   12 Mr. Hitt worked for years (2) (3)Hoping to reach his (4)*goal*.

1 Cd 2 j 3 k 4 b 5 e   13 Ed (2)*usually* does (3)*good* work (4) (5)Surely he is a strong candidate.

1 S 2 k 3 a 4 e   14 Surmounting (2)*great* difficulties (3) (4)She became a success.

1 Cd 2 b 3 e 4 g   15 Kay wanted to help (2) (3)However (4)*she* had homework.

Plain English Handbook, 20–23, 31–45, 52, 490, 495, 497, 499.

SCORE _____ (Top Score 100)

UNIT II
Verbs
INVENTORY 2

I. *Transitive and Intransitive Verbs*

10 Points

If the verb in the sentence is transitive, write **vt** before the sentence. If it is intransitive, write **vi.**

EXAMPLE: *vt* Have those girls been invited to the party?

vt 1 Did Fred help the girls with the program last week?

vt 2 Alice and Roger had been gathering tomatoes from the garden.

vt 3 Did you see Henry and George at the meeting last night?

vi 4 The sailplane soared gracefully above the hills.

vi 5 Have the others gone to the soccer match?

vt 6 Have all the tickets been sold so early in the day?

vt 7 Jan should have written those invitations yesterday.

vi 8 Dinner tasted good after our long walk to camp.

vt 9 Those other boys should have been helping Tom and me.

vt 10 Marie might have brought these pictures to us.

Plain English Handbook, 173–178, 180, 212, 213.

II. *Tenses of Verbs*

15 Points   105

Before each sentence write the correct tense form of the verb in parentheses.

EXAMPLE: _____*had seen*_____ Elaine and I (**see** — past perfect) that famous picture before.

_____ate_____ 1 The children (**eat** — past) the candy that we gave them.

_____swam_____ 2 The younger boys (**swim** — past) until they were exhausted.

_____has gone_____ 3 Dave (**go** — present perfect) to New Orleans with his family.

_____lie_____ 4 The kittens often (**lie** — present) in front of the fire.

_____rose_____ 5 The sun (**rise** — past) before we had finished breakfast.

_____had written_____ 6 Hal (**write** — past perfect) his assigned theme before school began.

_____had come_____ 7 Bob (**come** — past perfect) before we left the party.

_____has given_____ 8 Our music teacher (**give** — present perfect) us these concert tickets.

_____did_____ 9 Beth and she (**do** — past) their very best to win.

_____had lain_____ 10 My jacket (**lie** — past perfect) on the ground all night.

had lain 11 The stonemasons (**lay** — past perfect) heavy stones on the wall.

sat 12 Tom and Ken (**sit** — past) there until Bob returned.

have known 13 We (**know** — present perfect) Gary ever since he started school.

had run 14 Larry surely (**run** — past perfect) a good race at the meet.

has taken 15 Pat (**take** — present perfect) her report to class.

Plain English Handbook, 190–196, 204, 207, 216, 217.

III. *Using Verbs* 25 Points

Correct each incorrect verb form by writing the correct form on the line before the sentence. There may be more than one incorrect verb in some sentences. If there is no incorrect verb, write **C**. It may help you to cross out the incorrect word.

EXAMPLE: _____*Were*_____ ~~Was~~ Helen and her cousin here when you came?

go gone 1 There ~~goes~~ Nan and Jean, and the others have already ~~went~~. (239, 204)

are 2 Mrs. Scott is one of those managers who ~~is~~ always ready to listen. (241)

_C_ 3 Neither Kay nor her roommates were present when Don and he came. (238, 204)

lay 4 Bill and I ~~laid~~ down on the ground and rested. (217)

run was 5 Max had ~~ran~~ a good race although the number of contestants ~~were~~ large. (204, 244)

_C_ 6 The coach gave us full instructions before the game began. (204)

rose 7 After I came into the room, he ~~raised~~ to his feet. (204, 216, 217)

were 8 Either Jo or the boys ~~was~~ to stay after the others had gone. (238, 204)

were 9 Jed did well in the game, but you ~~was~~ the real star. (216, 260)

begun 10 We had already ~~began~~ work when Tim came. (204, 216)

thinks I 11 Neither the girls nor Ted ~~think~~ it is ~~me~~ who sent the letter. (238, 180)

has 12 Ben does not know which one of the messengers ~~have~~ gone to get Al. (246)

were came 13 I think there ~~was~~ five of us who ~~come~~ in late. (239, 204)

were done 14 If Bob ~~was~~ chairperson, he'd not do as others have ~~did~~. (256, 204)

doesn't 15 Joan was here when Leo left, but she ~~don't~~ know where he is. (197)

given 16 Have Freda and he ~~gave~~ the money to you? (216)

lay 17 The cat came into the room and ~~laid~~ down beside Kathy. (204, 217)

did 18 Mr. Carman, as well as his friends, liked what we ~~done~~. (236, 204)

Are 19 ~~Is~~ Bill and Joe ready to go, now that their work is done? (247, 216)

were 20 When we won the game, our team ~~was~~ given individual awards. (240)

106

UNIT III
Substantives, Modifiers, and Connectives
INVENTORY 3

I. Using Substantives   30 Points

Correct each incorrect noun or pronoun by writing the correct form on the line before the sentence. It may help you to cross out the incorrect word.

EXAMPLE: _____*she*_____ Are you sure it was ~~her~~ who came with Beth and him?   (152, 153)

she
_____ 1 It was ~~her~~ who made the schedules for us students.   (152, 157)

he
_____ 2 Joan and ~~him~~ are the two who are to go with Bob and me.   (149, 153)

who
_____ 3 She is a teacher ~~whom~~ you will find always helps us students.   (159, 157)

he
_____ 4 Is it ~~him~~ who is to go with Tom and me?   (152, 153)

us
_____ 5 It was Dick and she whom she asked to help ~~we~~ beginners.   (152, 160, 157)

her
_____ 6 He and I think that every girl will do ~~their~~ best to win.   (149, 164)

her
_____ 7 It was Jim and he whom we saw with Jill and ~~she~~.   (149, 160, 153)

me
_____ 8 Mr. Webb sent Tom and ~~I~~ the tickets for us students.   (154, 157)

we
_____ 9 All ~~us~~ members should help our club to keep its lead.   (151, 165)

him
_____10 Ed and he have the new caps for all us boys but Bo and ~~he~~.   (149, 157, 156)

she
_____11 Dick and he act much younger than Sue and ~~her~~.   (149, 148)

she
_____12 Could it have been ~~her~~ who sent the books for Ruth and me?   (152, 153)

men's
_____13 It must be Bob and he who work in the ~~mens'~~ shop.   (152, 159, 122)

his
_____14 Every man should send ~~their~~ ideas to Don or me.   (164, 153)

him
_____15 It was Todd and she who saw Pat and ~~he~~ at the boat show.   (152, 159, 153)

us
_____16 Here come Dad and she to go with ~~we~~ friends to the show.   (149, 157)

us
_____17 Do Kenny and he have the invitations for ~~we~~ girls?   (149, 157)

father-in-law's
_____18 It was Bess who came in my ~~father's-in-law~~ car.   (159, 123)

she
_____19 Leo and he think that Beth and ~~her~~ will invite us boys.   (149, 157)

its
_____20 Mrs. Hill helped the club to write ~~their~~ constitution.   (165)

he
_____21 Was it Joe and ~~him~~ who sent the record to Nita and me?   (152, 153)

who
_____22 She is one ~~whom~~ we think is a friend to all us students.   (159, 157)

her
_____23 All we girls but Tina and ~~she~~ were at the rally.   (151, 156)

us
_____24 It wasn't she who brought ~~we~~ boys the bad news.   (152, 155)

_us_
————— 25 Most of we ushers think it was Sal with Kay and her. (157, 153)

_he_
————— 26 No, it wasn't him whom you met with Dan and her. (152, 160, 153)

their
————— 27 Did the glee club have its robes cleaned? (165)

_me_
————— 28 Who do you think sent Betsy and I that funny card? (159, 154)

their
————— 29 Tom and I think that the students should give they're opinion. (149, 146)

who
————— 30 It is she whom we think should help Dave with the program. (152, 159)

II. *Modifiers and Connectives*

20 Points

Correct each incorrect adjective, adverb, preposition, or conjunction by writing the correct form on the line before the sentence. It may help you to cross out the incorrect word.

EXAMPLE: ——————— We students certainly make less mistakes in English now. (306)
(above line: _fewer_)

unless
————— 1 Ted can't win except he does his footwork more carefully. (370, 311)

surely
————— 2 He is the older of the two and he sure skates well. (296, 311, 329)

better
————— 3 Kay swims well, but Lou is the best swimmer of the two. (329, 296)

confident
————— 4 Anna looked confidently and she surely danced well. (289, 329)

anywhere
————— 5 Joe was really upset because he could not find his hat anywheres. (311, 330)

heavier
————— 6 Fred is not nearly so tall as Herb, but he is the heaviest of the two. (310, 296)

well
————— 7 Jo was somewhat upset, but she read her part good. (334, 329)

behind
————— 8 The book fell in back of the desk as I came into the room. (363, 357)

with
————— 9 I don't feel bad because Henry differs from me in my views. (289, 360)

surely no
(not any) ——10 There is surely not no reason for her going with them. (311, 336)

from
————11 Your pen is different than mine, but it is the better of the two. (337, 296)

really
————12 Hank is real intelligent, but he does his work carelessly. (311)

differently
————13 Tim is the better athlete of the two, but he should have played different. (296, 311)

from
————14 These cakes are different than those, but they do look good. (337, 289)

bad
————15 The river looked beautiful but it smelled badly. (289)

somewhat
————16 Al is some taller than we, and he is the oldest of the four. (334, 295)

anyone
_(was no one)_17 She behaved so rudely that there wasn't no one to defend her. (311, 336)

that
————18 Did you read where it was to get somewhat colder? (380, 334)

within
————19 He worked carefully and finished the job inside of an hour. (311, 356)

bad
————20 Dick surely played well, but he feels badly about losing. (311, 329, 289)

108

SCORE ——————— (Top Score 50)

UNIT IV
Sentence Structure
INVENTORY 4

I. *Sentence Parts* 20 Points

Indicate whether the italicized group of words in each sentence is a phrase or a clause by writing **P** or **C** on the first line. On the second line, rewrite the italicized group of words, changing each phrase to a clause and each clause to a phrase. (Answers may vary.)

EXAMPLE: C _____ *Waiting for John,* _____ While I *waited for John,* I washed the dishes.

P who hopes to be an artist, 1 Bess, *hoping to be an artist*, is studying painting.

C standing next to Ms. Webb. 2 The guest of honor is the man *who is standing next to Ms. Webb.*

C Driving down the turnpike, 3 *As we drove down the turnpike*, we saw many antique cars.

P who is wearing blue shorts 4 The girl *wearing blue shorts* is my sister.

C to go to Africa someday. 5 Ellen hopes *that she may go to Africa someday.*

P As she scrambled over the fence, 6 *Scrambling over the fence*, she saw the bull bearing down on her.

C After finishing my studies, 7 *After I finished my studies*, I fell into bed.

P As he ran to catch the bus, 8 *Running to catch the bus*, Jim fell and turned his ankle.

C Standing on the beach, 9 *As we stood on the beach*, we saw the *China Clipper* come into port.

P who have a sense of humor. 10 I admire people *with a sense of humor.*

Plain English Handbook, 387–409, 422.

II. *Sentence Effectiveness* 10 Points

Each item consists of two expressions of the same thought. On the line before the sentence number, write **A** or **B** to indicate which is the better sentence.

EXAMPLE: B **A** The juniors are working diligently. Hoping to sell all the tickets.
B The juniors, hoping to sell all the tickets, are working diligently.

A 1 **A** By working early and late, the painters finished the job on time.
B By working early and late, the job was completed on time.

A 2 **A** Jim said, "Bob, we've appointed you chairperson."
B Jim told Bob that he had been appointed chairperson.

B 3 **A** Calvin Davis is our star athlete, and he jogs to school every morning.
B Calvin Davis, our star athlete, jogs to school every morning.

B 4 **A** While we were in mountain country, many pine forests were seen.
B While we were in mountain country, we saw many pine forests.

B 5 **A** James enjoys team sports. Particularly football and basketball.
B James enjoys team sports, particularly football and basketball.

109

_A_ 6 **A** Looking far out to sea, we saw many ships.

    B Looking far out to sea, many ships were seen.

_B_ 7 **A** Everyone was happy. When we won the plaque.

    B Everyone was happy when we won the plaque.

_A_ 8 **A** In one of the shops Kay saw a hat which she liked.

    B Kay saw a hat in one of the shops which she liked.

_A_ 9 **A** When we were at the beach, we spent much time swimming.

    B When we were at the beach, much time was spent swimming.

_A_ 10 **A** Alice studies music seriously because she hopes to become a conductor.

    B Alice studies music seriously. Because she hopes to become a conductor.

Plain English Handbook, 433, 434, 436, 438, 439, 446, 447, 452, 455.

III. *Words in the Sentence* 20 Points

Correct each incorrectly used word by writing the correct form on the line before the sentence. If there is no incorrect word, write **C** before the sentence.

EXAMPLE: _____*ought*_____ He ~~had ought~~ to drive slower in the city. (225)

well
_____ 1 Eileen surely looked nervous, but she talked ~~good.~~ (311, 289, 329)

was
_____ 2 When Hugh and I came, neither Sue nor Clare ~~were~~ here. (149, 204, 237)

C
_____ 3 As I sat down, he rose to his feet and began to talk. (204, 217)

were
_____ 4 There are some of us boys who think that you ~~was~~ wrong. (239, 157, 260)

have
_____ 5 It might ~~of~~ been Pepe whom you saw with her. (230, 160)

who
_____ 6 Are Faye and she the girls ~~whom~~ you think will go too? (149, 159)

let
_____ 7 The principal would not ~~leave~~ us sell the tickets. (227)

from
_____ 8 Your outline is different ~~than~~ mine, but it is the better one. (337, 296)

are
_____ 9 Either Ms. Howe or the secretaries ~~is~~ to make out the schedule. (238)

go
_____ 10 There ~~goes~~ Mrs. DelRosa and the stage crew to set the stage for us dancers. (239, 217, 157)

thinks
_____ 11 Each one of the teachers ~~think~~ that he is the chairperson. (242)

should
_____ 12 We ~~had ought to~~ invite Lynn to our party. (225)

doesn't
_____ 13 If I were she, I'd ask Tonio why he ~~don't~~ join us. (256, 152, 197)

whom
_____ 14 Was it Ruth and he ~~who~~ you saw with Bill and her? (152, 160, 153)

us
_____ 15 Gail and she have invited ~~we~~ boys to the party. (149, 155)

C
_____ 16 Was it Maria who sent the books to Juan and me? (153)

anyone
_____ 17 There wasn't ~~no one~~ here when I came. (239, 336, 204)

basketfuls
_____ 18 While Don was here, he gathered six ~~basketsful~~ of apples. (87)

fewer
_____ 19 She makes ~~less~~ errors in math than her cousin. (306, 148)

within
_____ 20 Ben or they are to come ~~inside of~~ an hour. (238, 356)

SCORE _____ **(Top Score 50)**

110

UNIT V
Composition and the Use of Words
INVENTORY 5

I. *Paragraphs, Outlines, and Letters* 15 Points

On the line at the left write the number of the bold-faced word or expression that makes the statement true.

EXAMPLE: __1__ End punctuation in the heading is ¹not required/²required. (593)

__2__ 1 The sentences of a paragraph are ¹loosely/²closely related in thought. (541)

__2__ 2 In dialogue each speech is ¹set off by dashes/²separately paragraphed. (542)

__2__ 3 The topic sentence is placed ¹first/²anywhere in the paragraph. (544)

__2__ 4 Proper arrangement of sentences in a paragraph is called ¹unity/²coherence. (549)

__1__ 5 Sticking to the subject in a paragraph is ¹unity/²emphasis. (548)

__2__ 6 Topics of an outline should be arranged in ¹just any/²logical order. (578)

__2__ 7 The business letter has ¹five/²six parts. (590)

__1__ 8 Careful writers use ¹few/²many abbreviations in letters. (591)

__2__ 9 The ¹first/²last item of the heading is the date. (592)

__2__ 10 If a salutation consists of *dear* preceded by *my*, ¹both words are capitalized/²only the first word is capitalized. (595)

__1__ 11 A ¹colon/²comma is placed after the salutation of a business letter. (597)

__1__ 12 The participial closing is ¹little/²much used by careful writers. (599)

__2__ 13 In the complimentary close ¹each/²only the first word is capitalized. (599)

__1__ 14 The signature should be followed by ¹no punctuation/²a period. (600)

__1__ 15 A ¹comma/²dash should follow the salutation of a friendly letter. (617)

111

II. *Faulty Expressions in the Sentence* 10 Points

On the line at the left write the number of the bold-faced expression that is correct or more appropriate.

EXAMPLE: __2__ Almost all the officers ¹suspicioned/²suspected the stranger of the theft.

__2__ 1 Both of the gentlemen were dressed ¹formerly/²formally.

__1__ 2 It is ¹strange/²funny that you didn't see the car in time to stop.

__2__ 3 Those stragglers have only a short ¹ways/²way to go now.

__2__ 4 The volunteers worked very hard in ¹setting up/²arranging the party.

__1__ 5 He was ¹angry/²mad because I would go no further with the plans he presented.

__2__ 6 You ¹had ought to/²ought to do your schoolwork before you go.

__1__ 7 I think it would be ¹all right/²alright to lend Joan's book to Jack.

__1__ 8 You will be ¹rather/²kind of tired by the end of a full day of hiking.

__1__ 9 The change in temperature is ¹likely/²liable to help the spring wheat crop.

__1__ 10 How can we ¹teach/²learn them to be more careful?

Plain English Handbook, 665–674.

III. *Using Words in the Sentence* 25 Points

On the line at the left write the number of the bold-faced word that is the correct form to use in the sentence.

EXAMPLE: <u>2</u> We should trade at ¹**Wall's**/²**Wall** and Hill's Store. (124)

<u>2</u> 1 The members, not the president, ¹**is**/²**are** making the arrangements. (261)

<u>1</u> 2 The cakes didn't look good, but they tasted very ¹**good**/²**well**. (289, 312)

<u>2</u> 3 Neither their language nor their customs are different ¹**than**/²**from** ours. (337)

<u>2</u> 4 Jack is one of those people who ¹**is**/²**are** always friendly. (241)

<u>1</u> 5 Tom and he picked ten ¹**basketfuls**/²**basketsful** of apples. (87)

<u>2</u> 6 Were you here when she told about ¹**Tom**/²**Tom's** winning the race? (127)

<u>2</u> 7 They ¹**swum**/²**swam** to shore after their canoe sank. (204)

<u>1</u> 8 We ¹**gave**/²**give** the message to her as soon as we saw her. (204, 216)

<u>2</u> 9 I am sure that Sandra will go with Marie and ¹**she**/²**her**. (153)

<u>2</u> 10 Is it she ¹**who**/²**whom** you asked to help with the decorations? (160)

<u>2</u> 11 If I were he, I'd ¹**set**/²**sit** there and wait. (204, 217)

<u>1</u> 12 When Dick and I ¹**came**/²**come**, you were not here. (204, 216)

<u>1</u> 13 He feels ¹**bad**/²**badly** because Joe is angry with him. (289, 312)

<u>1</u> 14 One of the identical twins stood ¹**behind**/²**in back of** the other's desk. (363)

<u>1</u> 15 There ¹**go**/²**goes** Alicia and Mary with Chico and him. (239)

<u>1</u> 16 He may not feel ¹**that**/²**as** he can do as we suggest. (379)

<u>1</u> 17 She cannot do ¹**differently**/²**different** unless we tell her. (311)

<u>2</u> 18 John will not finish ¹**except**/²**unless** we help him. (370)

<u>2</u> 19 Send ¹**whomever**/²**whoever** will assist Grace and him. (161)

<u>2</u> 20 Neither Jack ¹**or**/²**nor** Julio will sell his bicycle. (378)

<u>2</u> 21 ¹**Was**/²**Were** Bill and Ruth with Ann and him? (247)

<u>1</u> 22 The author ¹**doesn't**/²**don't** explain how the thieves were caught. (197)

<u>1</u> 23 We ¹**ate**/²**eat** our breakfast long before the sun rose. (204)

<u>1</u> 24 Jack and ¹**he**/²**him** must have gone on without you two. (149)

<u>2</u> 25 It might have been they who brought ¹**we**/²**us** officers the tickets. (155)

SCORE _____ (Top Score 50)

112

Final Inventory/A

I. *Sentence Sense* 10 Points

On the line preceding each group of words, write **o** if the group is not a complete sentence; write **1** if the group is one complete sentence; or write **2** if the group is two sentences incorrectly written as one.

EXAMPLE: __o__ Sitting at the tables in the study hall.

__1__ 1 Cheering wildly, we watched Hex make a touchdown.

__0__ 2 Working, planning, and hoping that a college education would be possible.

__1__ 3 Bring your new tennis racket to school tomorrow.

__0__ 4 Because she had worked so long and so faithfully at perfecting her butterfly stroke.

__2__ 5 It was the most thrilling game of the season our team played well.

__1__ 6 Although the work was difficult, Bill completed the job on time.

__0__ 7 Went fishing with Henry and Joe last Saturday.

__2__ 8 We will meet again on Wednesday, Jorge Gómez will preside.

__1__ 9 When will the performance begin?

__0__ 10 While we waited impatiently for the big game to begin.

Plain English Handbook, 1–4, 33–37.

II. *Classifying Sentences and Parts of Speech* 30 Points

On the first line preceding each sentence, indicate its class by writing **S** for simple, **Cd** for compound, or **Cx** for complex. On the next two lines indicate the part of speech of each of the two italicized words by writing **n** for noun, **pron** for pronoun, **adj** for adjective, **adv** for adverb, **v** for verb, **prep** for preposition, or **conj** for conjunction. Class the conjunctive adverb as a conjunction.

EXAMPLE: __Cx__ __pron__ __conj__ *She* came *before* we left the meeting.

__Cd__ __conj__ __adv__ 1 We played a fast game, *but* we did *not* win.

__S__ __n__ __v__ 2 *Harry* wrote and *directed* the school play.

__Cx__ __adj__ __v__ 3 *These* perennial plants that you gave me *need* watering.

__S__ __prep__ __conj__ 4 All the lifeguards have gone *but* Hal *and* Glenda.

__Cd__ __conj__ __pron__ 5 The others are here somewhere, *but* I have not seen *them*.

__Cd__ __adj__ __adv__ 6 Mary looked *thrilled*, and she performed her part *well*.

__S__ __prep__ __pron__ 7 Working *at* his job, Joe did not see *us* come in.

__S__ __adv__ __n__ 8 Do you *ever* have trouble with your *pronouns*?

__Cx__ __pron__ __v__ 9 *This* is the rock record that Bob *gave* me.

__Cd__ __n__ __conj__ 10 He does all his *work* well; *therefore*, he surely will succeed.

Plain English Handbook, 20–23, 38–45, 52, 138–140, 320.

III. *Substantives and Verbs*   60 Points

Each sentence has three incorrect words. Correct each incorrect noun, pronoun, or verb by writing the correct forms (in their right order) on the lines before the sentence.

he	were	sitting

EXAMPLE: Sue and ~~him~~ ~~was~~ ~~setting~~ on the porch.   (149, 247, 204)

have	their	whom

1 The band ~~has~~ ordered ~~its~~ instruments from the shop-keeper ~~who~~ you suggested.   (240, 165, 160)

he	her	them

2 It is ~~him~~ who will bring the visitor and ~~she~~ to ~~they.~~   (96, 160, 153, 106)

he	oxen	geese

3 It was ~~him~~ and I who saw the ~~oxes~~ and the ~~gooses~~.   (149, 160, 85, 84)

turkeys	Bell	has

4 The number of frozen ~~turkies~~ sold by ~~Bell's~~ and Hill's Market ~~have~~ decreased.   (81, 124, 244)

are	teaching	us

5 Mr. Lee is one of the coaches who is ~~learning~~ ~~we~~ team-mates some new plays.   (241, 227, 155)

he	is	club's

6 Neither our fathers nor ~~him~~ ~~are~~ able to attend the ~~clubs'~~ meeting.   (149, 238, 120)

caught	ran	his

7 Bill ~~catched~~ the ball and ~~run~~ for ~~his'~~ first touchdown.   (204, 146)

brothers-in-law	bushels	potatoes

8 My ~~brother-in-laws~~ and I dug six ~~bushel~~ of ~~potatos~~.   (86, 300, 78)

was	her	done

9 Neither Pat nor Jan ~~were~~ ready to give ~~their~~ report of what she had ~~did~~.   (237, 142, 164, 204, 216)

we	know	he

10 All ~~us~~ actors, as well as the director, ~~knows~~ that Paula acts better than ~~him~~.   (151, 236, 148)

trios	wives	have

11 The ~~trioes,~~ made up of husbands and ~~wifes,~~ should ~~of~~ sung at the P.T.A. dinner.   (79, 82, 230)

sitting	I	lay

12 The children were ~~setting~~ on the ground while Joe and ~~me~~ ~~laid~~ on the porch.   (217, 149)

her	me	she

13 John thought ~~she~~ to be ~~I~~. I am often thought to be ~~her~~.   (272, 273, 274)

were	were	clown's

14 You ~~was~~ the only one who laughed as if you ~~was~~ amused by the ~~clowns~~ antics.   (260, 258, 120)

her	me	bucketfuls

15 The farmer sold ~~she~~ and ~~I~~ two ~~bucketsful~~ of blueberries.   (154, 87)

was	father-in-law's	sheep

16 Four hundred dollars ~~were~~ paid for his ~~father's-in-law~~ share of the ~~sheeps~~.   (245, 123, 89)

Who	girls'	boys'
	(or omit	

17 ~~Whom~~ did you say would direct the sophomore ~~girl's~~ and ~~boy's~~ games?   (159, 121)

Don't	he	should had)

18 ~~Doesn't~~ Marta and ~~him~~ think they ~~had ought~~ to come tomorrow?   (197, 149, 225)

me	was	Mary's

19 Everyone but Hank and ~~I~~ ~~were~~ surprised at ~~Mary~~ winning the prize.   (156, 242, 270)

Alice's	were	berries

20 ~~Alice~~ and Jim's hands ~~was~~ stained by the ~~berrys~~.   (125, 197, 80)

IV. *Modifiers and Connectives*

Make all necessary corrections in the use of adjectives, adverbs, prepositions, and conjunctions in the manner indicated in the example.

EXAMPLE: ___*That*___ ___*other*___ ~~That there~~ house looks better than any house in town. (674, 298)

whether	surely	1 I don't know ~~if~~ he will come, but I ~~sure~~ hope he does. (381, 311)
smaller	well	2 The ~~smallest~~ of the two boys skates very ~~good~~. (296, 329)
that	easily	3 I read ~~where~~ the workers can ~~easy~~ finish the pool by June. (380, 339)
older	so	4 The ~~oldest~~ of my two cousins is not ~~as~~ tall as you. (296, 310)
as	any	5 Behave ~~like~~ you were taught or you won't have ~~no~~ friends. (372, 336)
This	somewhat	6 ~~These~~ kind of skate is ~~some~~ better than mine. (302, 334)
by	besides	7 We shall be accompanied ~~with~~ three other boys ~~beside~~ my brother. (355, 353)
rather	with	8 Ed was ~~kind of~~ angry ~~at~~ Jo for taking the car. (333, 351)
to	surely	9 If they will agree ~~with~~ our plan, we will ~~sure~~ have a good time. (350, 311)
fewer	of game *(or omit more)*	10 No ~~less~~ than ten people can play that kind ~~of a game~~. (306, 307)
Nowhere	tasty	11 ~~Nowheres~~ can you find a steak more ~~tastier~~ than this. (330, 295)
well	rather	12 Our senior team played ~~good~~, and the other team played ~~sort of~~ badly. (329, 333)
anyone else	so	13 Jane is taller than ~~anyone~~ in her class, but she is not ~~as~~ tall as her teacher. (298, 310)
well	beautiful	14 Kay swims ~~good~~, and her strokes look ~~beautifully~~. (329, 289)
Almost	somewhat	15 ~~Most~~ all of us feel ~~some~~ better after a trip. (328, 334)
anyone	within	16 There wasn't ~~no one~~ who finished ~~inside~~ an hour. (336, 356)
last six	as	17 He told us to omit the ~~six last~~ pages ~~like~~ we expected. (303, 372)
caught only	an	18 Bob ~~only caught~~ four bass and ~~a~~ eel while fishing. (340, 286)
differently	bad	19 If he had behaved ~~different~~, he would not feel ~~badly~~ now. (311, 289)
that	with	20 Sue did not feel ~~as~~ she could part ~~from~~ the money required for a new dress. (379, 362)
from	of car	21 This car is different ~~than~~ the old one, but I don't like this kind ~~of a car~~. (361, 307)
nor	with	22 Neither Jim ~~or~~ Mary differs ~~from~~ me in political beliefs. (378, 360)
off the	behind	23 The vase fell ~~off of the~~ table and rolled ~~in back of~~ the door. (364, 363)
is	from	24 This kind of program ~~are~~ different ~~than~~ the ones we watched last year. (302, 361)
between	as	25 Helen divided the candy ~~among~~ the twins ~~like~~ Mother told her. (354, 372)

V. Sentence Effectiveness   5 Points

Each item consists of two expressions of the same thought. On the line before the number of the sentence, write **A** or **B** to indicate which is the better sentence.

EXAMPLE: <u>A</u>   **A** Jim likes to play games, especially tennis and baseball.
                 B Jim likes to play games. Especially tennis and baseball.

<u>B</u> 1   **A** Driving through the deep snow, many stalled cars were seen.
            B Driving through the deep snow, we saw many stalled cars.

<u>B</u> 2   **A** Suzanne saw a bike in a shop which she liked very much.
            B In a shop Suzanne saw a bike which she liked very much.

<u>B</u> 3   **A** Larry told Bob that he had been made the new goalkeeper.
            B Larry told Bob, "You have been made the new goalkeeper."

<u>A</u> 4   **A** Hank and Charles had a good time while they were in Canada.
            B Hank and Charles had a good time. While they were in Canada.

<u>B</u> 5   **A** Jack Norton is an excellent athlete, and he works on a farm in the summer.
            B Jack Norton, who is an excellent athlete, works on a farm in the summer.

Plain English Handbook, 433, 436, 438, 446, 447, 451, 452.

VI. Capitalization and Punctuation   45 Points

Indicate the punctuation and capitalization needed at each point marked by a number in parentheses. Indicate a semicolon rather than a period wherever possible. Use the following key:

a — capital letter	**c** — comma	**e** — semicolon	**g** — question mark
b — small letter	**d** — period	**f** — quotation marks	**h** — hyphen

EXAMPLE: 1 <u>*c*</u> 2 <u>*c*</u> 3 <u>*d*</u> 4 <u>*a*</u> 5 <u>*d*</u>   Ed[1] Faye[2] and Al go to East [3]high [4]school[5]   (504, 471, 486)

1 <u>a</u> 2 <u>a</u> 3 <u>c</u> 4 <u>c</u> 5 <u>a</u>   1 On [1]friday, [2]july 23[3] 1972[4] we left for the [5]canadian wilds.   (469, 502, 468)

1 <u>c</u> 2 <u>c</u> 3 <u>h</u> 4 <u>c</u> 5 <u>e</u>   2 Al is[1] I believe[2] a hard[3]working[4] clever senior[5] he deserves the award.   (500, 532, 505, 490)

1 <u>c</u> 2 <u>f</u> 3 <u>a</u> 4 <u>f</u> 5 <u>g</u>   3 Did you hear Bill say[1] [2][3]we must win this game[4][5]   (501, 507, 466, 514, 529)

1 <u>b</u> 2 <u>a</u> 3 <u>c</u> 4 <u>a</u> 5 <u>d</u>   4 Last [1]Summer we visited [2]memphis[3] [4]tennessee[5]   (470, 468, 500, 486)

1 <u>b</u> 2 <u>f</u> 3 <u>a</u> 4 <u>c</u> 5 <u>f</u>   5 My [1]Mother said, [2][3]if you want to go[4] you should pack now.[5]   (482, 507, 466, 497)

1 <u>a</u> 2 <u>c</u> 3 <u>c</u> 4 <u>c</u> 5 <u>e</u>   6 [1]that farmer raises corn[2] rye[3] oats[4] and barley[5] however, wheat is his principal crop.   (464, 504, 490)

1 <u>c</u> 2 <u>a</u> 3 <u>a</u> 4 <u>c</u> 5 <u>a</u>   7 Margaret Mitchell[1] who wrote [2]*gone with the* [3]*wind*[4] lived in the [5]south.   (499, 478, 474)

1 <u>h</u> 2 <u>a</u> 3 <u>a</u> 4 <u>a</u> 5 <u>d</u>   8 Twenty[1]six students from [2]wade [3]high [4]school are trying for the scholarship[5]   (534, 471, 486)

1 <u>b</u> 2 <u>a</u> 3 <u>a</u> 4 <u>e</u> 5 <u>d</u>   9 Mr. Black lives [1]North of [2]kansas [3]city[4] however, he works in St[5] Joseph.   (474, 468, 490, 487)

SCORE _____ (Top Score 200)

Final Inventory/B

I. *Sentence Sense* \qquad\qquad\qquad\qquad\qquad\qquad\qquad\qquad\qquad\qquad 10 Points

On the line preceding each group of words, write **0** if the group is not a complete sentence; write **1** if the group is one complete sentence; or write **2** if the group is two sentences incorrectly written as one.

EXAMPLE: <u>0</u> When the dentist had finished.

<u>2</u> 1 I am going to the circus tomorrow, I am going with Jim.

<u>1</u> 2 By working hard, Bill has accomplished much.

<u>0</u> 3 Running to catch the bounding ball.

<u>1</u> 4 Expecting to become a noted author, Alice writes many stories.

<u>0</u> 5 After Fred had finished his work and had gone home.

<u>0</u> 6 Spent last summer in the mountains of New Hampshire.

<u>2</u> 7 Hal is captain of the hockey team all his teammates like him.

<u>1</u> 8 When did Juanita say that she would arrive?

<u>0</u> 9 Unless he does better work in English.

<u>0</u> 10 Because the day was hot and humid.

Plain English Handbook, 1–4, 33–37.

II. *Classifying Sentences and Parts of Speech* \qquad\qquad\qquad\qquad\qquad 30 Points

On the first line preceding each sentence, indicate its class by writing **S** for simple, **Cd** for compound, or **Cx** for complex. On the next two lines, indicate the part of speech of each of the two italicized words by writing **n** for noun, **pron** for pronoun, **adj** for adjective, **adv** for adverb, **v** for verb, **prep** for preposition, or **conj** for conjunction. Class the conjunctive adverb as a conjunction.

EXAMPLE: <u>S</u> <u>n</u> <u>adv</u> *Terry* and he go sailing *nearly* every day.

<u>S</u> <u>v</u> <u>adj</u> 1 Miss Lind *liked* our program, particularly the *musical* numbers.

<u>Cd</u> <u>adj</u> <u>adv</u> 2 The pumpkin pie looked *good*, but we did *not* taste it.

<u>Cd</u> <u>adj</u> <u>conj</u> 3 Hank Wilson is *friendly*; *however*, somehow he is not very popular.

<u>S</u> <u>conj</u> <u>prep</u> 4 Ellen *and* the others have gone *to* the show.

<u>S</u> <u>adv</u> <u>adv</u> 5 There are *only* ten people in our club *now*.

<u>Cx</u> <u>n</u> <u>n</u> 6 Mary thinks that *"but"* is always a *conjunction*.

<u>Cx</u> <u>pron</u> <u>pron</u> 7 *This* is the best book *I* have ever read.

<u>Cx</u> <u>pron</u> <u>adj</u> 8 We drove very slowly after *we* reached the *school* grounds.

<u>Cx</u> <u>adj</u> <u>conj</u> 9 I must give *this* table a smooth finish *before* I leave.

<u>Cx</u> <u>v</u> <u>prep</u> 10 If we *work* hard, we can finish this job *before* noon.

Plain English Handbook, 20–23, 38–45, 52, 138–140, 320.

Correct each incorrect noun, pronoun, or verb by writing the correct forms on the lines preceding the sentence.

EXAMPLE: _____*she*_____ _____*were*_____ _____*came*_____ Dick and ~~her was~~ there when I ~~come.~~ (149, 247, 204, 216)

have	her	me	1 Bob could ~~of~~ helped ~~she~~ and ~~I~~ if he had been on time. (230, 153)
are	brought	her	2 Joy, one of those people who ~~is~~ always active, and Pam each ~~brung their~~ racket. (241, 204, 163)
was	given	us	3 Twenty dollars ~~were gave~~ to the chairperson to help ~~we~~ members finance the next dance. (245, 204, 157)
Were	he	gave	4 ~~Was~~ Dick and ~~him~~ here when the coach ~~give~~ the new instructions? (247, 149, 204, 216)
children's	cries	officer's	5 The ~~childrens'~~ shrill ~~crys~~ attracted a police ~~officers~~ attention. (122, 80, 120)
thinks	were	she	6 Neither Frank nor she ~~think~~ that you ~~was~~ later than ~~her.~~ (237, 260, 148)
were	sitting	lay	7 A number of employees ~~was setting~~ on the steps while I ~~laid~~ on the grass. (244, 204, 217)
Doesn't	were	him	8 ~~Don't~~ Betty speak as if she ~~was~~ angry with Tom and ~~he?~~ (197, 258, 153)
he	she	who	9 It was ~~him~~ and ~~her whom~~ we believed would arrange the program. (152, 159)
I	her	blueberries	10 Ted and ~~me~~ saw Jim and ~~she~~ while they were picking ~~blueberrys.~~ (149, 153, 80)
We	is	drank	11 ~~Us~~ three ate ham and eggs, which ~~are~~ a good food, and ~~drunk~~ lemonade. (151, 247, 204)
come	he	us	12 There ~~comes~~ Bob and ~~him~~ to help ~~we~~ players with our forward passes. (239, 149, 157)
Jan's	torn	Tom's	13 ~~Jan~~ and Lou's new long skirts were ~~tore~~ by ~~Toms~~ dog. (125, 204, 120)
Who	ought to (should)	us	14 ~~Whom~~ do you think ~~had ought to~~ help ~~we~~ actors with the next play? (159, 225, 157)
their	have	whomever	15 To get ~~its~~ uniforms, the band ~~has~~ to go to ~~whoever~~ the director selects. (165, 240, 162)
were	him	teach	16 If I ~~was~~ there, I could help Pat and ~~he learn~~ Jan to swim. (256, 153, 227)
him	me	wants	17 Each member of the class except ~~he~~ and ~~I want~~ to go to the race. (153, 242)
was	Al's	bucketfuls	18 Neither the boys nor I ~~were~~ surprised by ~~Al~~ winning the ~~bucketsful~~ of pennies at the fair. (238, 270, 87)
ponies	sheep	calves	19 The Browns have ~~ponys, sheeps,~~ cows, and many ~~calfs~~ on their farm. (80, 89, 82)
We	boys'	brothers-in-law	20 ~~Us~~ organizers should invite the two ~~boy's brother-in-laws~~ to the picnic. (151, 121, 86)

118

IV. *Modifiers and Connectives*

Make all necessary corrections in the use of adjectives, adverbs, prepositions, and conjunctions in the manner indicated in the example.

EXAMPLE: __*saw only*__ __*from*__ I ~~only saw~~ one player with a bat different ~~than~~ mine. (340, 361)

__one (*or omit* Not)__ __differently__ 1 Not ~~none of~~ us would do the job ~~different.~~ (336, 311)

__to__ __between__ 2 I agree ~~with~~ Joanne's plan that we divide the work ~~among~~ the two of them. (350, 354)

__Between__ __easily__ 3 ~~Among~~ the two artists, the work will be completed ~~easy.~~ (354, 339)

__any__ __working only__ 4 There wasn't ~~no~~ reason for Ed's ~~only working~~ an hour. (336, 340)

__taller__ __behind__ 5 The ~~tallest~~ of the two ladders stands ~~in back of~~ the barn. (296, 363)

__in__ __easily__ 6 We should arrive ~~at~~ Toronto by noon ~~easy.~~ (352, 339)

__that__ __by__ 7 I saw in the local paper ~~where~~ Jo was accompanied ~~with~~ her mother on the trip. (380, 355)

__sweet__ __really__ 8 The flowers smell ~~sweetly~~, and they are ~~real~~ lovely. (289, 311)

__bad__ __anyone (*or omit* not)__ 9 Glenn feels ~~badly~~ about failing, but he hasn't ~~no one~~ to blame but himself. (289, 336)

__off the__ __into__ 10 The boy dived ~~off of the~~ dock ~~in~~ the lake. (364, 357)

__among__ __unless__ 11 She wouldn't divide the candy ~~between~~ the three children ~~except~~ they were quiet. (354, 370)

__promptly__ __well__ 12 Jan does her work ~~prompt~~, and she does it ~~good.~~ (311, 329)

__somewhat__ __nowhere__ 13 Dad feels ~~some~~ better, but he can go ~~nowheres~~ for a week. (334, 330)

__carefully__ __off the__ 14 If you drive ~~careful~~, the box should not fall ~~off of the~~ truck. (311, 364)

__Almost__ __this__ 15 ~~Most~~ all teenagers like ~~these~~ kind of movie. (328, 302)

__with__ __better__ 16 Joan differs ~~from~~ you about cars, and she believes this one is the ~~best~~ of the two. (360, 296)

__rather__ __with__ 17 He is ~~sort of~~ angry ~~at us~~ for leaving. (333, 351)

__whether__ __within__ 18 I do not know ~~if~~ he will come, but I hope he does arrive ~~inside of~~ an hour. (381, 356)

__last ten__ __as__ 19 We omitted the ~~ten last~~ pages ~~like~~ she said. (303, 372)

__so__ __surely__ 20 Bill is not ~~as~~ old as Jim, but he is ~~sure~~ more mature. (310, 311)

__Fewer__ __of play__ 21 ~~Less~~ than six members like that kind ~~of a play.~~ (306, 307)

__nor__ __well__ 22 Neither Dot ~~or~~ Hal dances ~~good~~ enough yet. (378, 329)

__clearly__ __distinctly__ 23 The lecturer spoke ~~clear~~ and ~~distinct.~~ (311)

__that__ __to__ 24 I don't feel ~~as~~ I can agree ~~with~~ your plan. (379, 350)

__Almost__ __somewhat__ 25 ~~Most~~ all of us are singing ~~kind of~~ better now. (328, 333)

V. *Sentence Effectiveness*   5 Points

Each item consists of two expressions of the same thought. On the line before the number of the sentence, write **A** or **B** to indicate which is the better sentence.

EXAMPLE: __B__ A Hank did some chores. Before he came to school today.
                  B Hank did some chores before he came to school today.

__A__ 1 A Playing games and singing songs, we enjoyed the evening.
          B Playing games and singing songs, the evening was enjoyed.

__B__ 2 A Nonita likes fruit. Particularly cherries.
          B Nonita likes fruit, particularly cherries.

__B__ 3 A Margaret told Louisa that she had been invited to the wedding.
          B Margaret said, "Louisa, I've been invited to the wedding."

__A__ 4 A Mary Matthews, the president of our class, has an aunt living in Paris.
          B Mary Matthews is the president of our class she has an aunt living in Paris.

__B__ 5 A Todd saw a picture in the exhibit which he thought was very odd.
          B In the exhibit Todd saw a picture which he thought was very odd.

Plain English Handbook, 433, 436, 438, 439, 445, 446, 451, 452.

VI. *Capitalization and Punctuation*   45 Points

Indicate the punctuation and capitalization needed at each point marked by a number in parentheses. Indicate a semicolon rather than a period wherever possible. Use the following key:

a — capital letter   c — comma   e — semicolon   g — question mark
b — small letter   d — period   f — quotation marks   h — hyphen

EXAMPLE: 1 *c* 2 *c* 3 *b* 4 *c* 5 *d*   No(1) Mary(2) my (3)Cousin(4) is from the (5)north. (498, 500, 482, 474)

1 a 2 a 3 c 4 b 5 d   1 Before I came to Sims (1)high (2)school(3) I went to a school (4)North of St(5) Louis. (471, 497, 474, 487)

1 c 2 c 3 c 4 h 5 e   2 Jane is(1) I believe(2) a capable(3) hard(4) working student(5) she deserves success. (500, 505, 532, 489)

1 a 2 b 3 a 4 c 5 b   3 Next (1)monday my (2)Mother and (3)i will visit Ruth Harris(4) my oldest (5)Cousin. (469, 482, 479, 500)

1 a 2 a 3 a 4 a 5 f   4 She asked, "(1)what can you tell us about the present (2)united (3)states (4)congress?(5) (466, 468, 471, 507)

1 a 2 b 3 c 4 a 5 g   5 When you were in the (1)south last (2)Spring(3) did you visit (4)atlanta(5) (474, 470, 497, 468, 529)

1 h 2 b 3 a 4 c 5 c   6 Twenty(1)six (2)Seniors have enrolled for (3)french(4) history(5) and English. (534, 471, 468, 504)

1 a 2 c 3 f 4 f 5 g   7 (1)did Bill say(2) (3)I'll be here early(4) (5) (464, 501, 507, 514)

1 c 2 b 3 a 4 a 5 a   8 No(1) our (2)History class isn't studying the (3)spanish-(4)american (5)war. (498, 471, 468)

1 b 2 b 3 e 4 c 5 c   9 Harry went to our (1)High (2)School(3) however he lives in Ames(4) Iowa(5) now. (471, 490, 500)

Final Inventory/C

I. *Sentence Sense* 10 Points

On the line before each group of words, write **0** if the group is not a complete sentence; write **1** if the group is one complete sentence; write **2** if the group is two sentences incorrectly written as one; or write **3** if the group is three sentences incorrectly written as one.

EXAMPLE: <u>0</u> Before the final plans had been completed.

<u>0</u> 1 Went to the organ recital with Johnnie last night.

<u>1</u> 2 After they have made the plans, they will report to the club.

<u>1</u> 3 That green house across the street is the one I like.

<u>0</u> 4 Have been waiting to see the new track coach.

<u>1</u> 5 Read Jane's latest letter when you have time.

<u>3</u> 6 Our club is planning a carnival everyone is to take part you must plan to go.

<u>1</u> 7 Hoping to win the state title, the team played its best.

<u>2</u> 8 Cindy is the president, she will appoint a new by-laws committee.

<u>0</u> 9 At the time when everyone was busy.

<u>0</u>10 Expecting to go to the Canadian Rockies.

Plain English Handbook, 1–4, 33–37.

II. *Essential Parts of the Sentence* 10 Points

On the first line before each sentence, write the simple subject. On the second line, write the simple predicate.

EXAMPLE: _____*work*_____ _____*Can be completed*_____ Can the work be completed soon?

<u>we</u> <u>looked</u> 1 Hearing a siren, we looked for a police car.

<u>Ben</u> <u>went</u> 2 Having eaten lunch, Ben went to play tennis.

<u>they</u> <u>Have forgotten</u> 3 Have they forgotten about the meeting?

<u>John</u> <u>Could have been told</u> 4 Could John have been told that I won?

<u>sound</u> <u>came</u> 5 From the hills came the sound of thunder.

Plain English Handbook, 3, 4, 13, 15.

III. *Classifying Sentences and Sentence Parts* 30 Points

On the first line classify the sentence as to form by writing **S** for simple, **Cd** for compound, **Cx** for complex, or **Cd-Cx** for compound-complex. On the second line indicate whether the italicized group of words is a phrase or a clause by writing **P** or **C**. On the third line indicate the use of the phrase or clause by writing **n** for noun, **adj** for adjective, or **adv** for adverb.

EXAMPLE: <u>Cd</u> <u>P</u> <u>adv</u> *In the garden* grew scarlet roses, and the air was fragrant.

<u>S</u> <u>P</u> <u>adj</u> 1 That boy *running down the street* stole the money.

<u>Cx</u> <u>C</u> <u>n</u> 2 The truth is *that she did her best*.

<u>S</u> <u>P</u> <u>adj</u> 3 The woman *seated on the platform* is our administrative principal.

Cx	C	adj	4 Quickly we accepted the offer *that he made.*
Cd-Cx	C	adv	5 We began the work, but we didn't finish *until you came.*
S	P	adv	6 Helen and I walked *around the block.*
Cd	P	adj	7 He told stories *of pioneer days,* and we listened.
S	P	n	8 *To accomplish a great task* requires much effort.
Cx	C	adv	9 The plane had left *before we reached the airport.*
Cx	C	adj	10 Great deeds are accomplished by those *who have ambition.*

Plain English Handbook, 389–416.

IV. *Defective Sentences*

5 Points

Each item consists of two expressions of the same thought. On the line before each number, write **A** or **B** to indicate which is the better sentence.

EXAMPLE: __A__ **A** Ms. Hernandez, a mathematics teacher, plays the organ.

B Ms. Hernandez is a mathematics teacher, and she plays the organ.

__A__ 1 **A** Walking swiftly, we soon reached our destination.

B Walking swiftly, our destination was soon reached.

__B__ 2 **A** As we drove through the park, we almost saw fifty buffaloes.

B As we drove through the park, we saw almost fifty buffaloes.

__B__ 3 **A** Nell told Jean that she had won the prize.

B Nell said, "Jean, you have won the prize."

__B__ 4 **A** Robert is intelligent and has ambition.

B Robert is intelligent and ambitious.

__B__ 5 **A** He held a spear in his hand that was made of wood.

B In his hand he held a spear that was made of wood.

Plain English Handbook, 340, 433, 439, 450, 451, 452.

V. *Capitalization and Punctuation in the Sentence*

45 Points

Indicate the changes needed in these sentences by writing the appropriate letter from the following key beside each number at the left.

a — capital letter	d — period	g — question mark	j — dash
b — small letter	e — semicolon	h — quotation marks	k — no change
c — comma	f — hyphen	i — colon	

EXAMPLE: 1 __b__ 2 __b__ 3 __d__ 4 __c__ 5 __d__   Last [1]Summer my [2]Mother went to [3]onawa[4] [5]iowa.   (470, 482, 468, 500)

1 __b__ 2 __i__ 3 __b__ 4 __a__ 5 __a__ 1 The [1]Juniors very much like the following subjects[2] [3]History, [4]french, and [5]english. (471, 493)

1 __c__ 2 __a__ 3 __d__ 4 __a__ 5 __g__ 2 Pam was on television on Thursday[1] [2]march 20[3] [4]did you see her[5] (502, 469, 445, 486, 464, 529)

1 __c__ 2 __h__ 3 __b__ 4 __h__ 5 __g__ 3 Who said[1] [2]The [3]Fall season is the best of all[4] [5] (501, 507, 470, 514)

1 __h__ 2 __a__ 3 __c__ 4 __g__ 5 __h__ 4 Jane asked, [1]Where were you during [2]christmas[3] Susan[4] [5] (507, 469, 500, 529, 514)

1 __d__ 2 __c__ 3 __b__ 4 __a__ 5 __e__ 5 Mrs[1] Orr[2] the [3]Superintendent of our schools, lived in the [4]east[5] however, she likes the West. (487, 500, 481, 474, 490)

1 __a__ 2 __a__ 3 __c__ 4 __c__ 5 __c__ 6 The trees in [1]oberon [2]park are gorgeous[3] especially the oaks[4] elms[5] and maples. (468, 484, 499, 504)

1 __c__ 2 __a__ 3 __c__ 4 __b__ 5 __g__ 7 Esther[1] did you see [2]miss Coleman[3] your [4]Mathematics teacher[5] (500, 481, 471, 529)

122

₁ _c_₂ _f_₃ _a_₄ _k_₅ _a_ 8 If you will check[1] you will find that there are fifty[2]six pages in [3]*exploring* [4]*the* [5]*sun.* (497, 534, 478)

₁ _f_₂ _k_₃ _j_₄ _c_₅ _c_ 9 We drove twenty[1]three miles [2]north, and there they were[3] Bob[4] Ernie[5] and Sandy. (534, 474, 523, 504)

VI. *Using Substantives and Verbs in the Sentence* 40 Points

On the lines at the left, write the numbers of the bold-faced words that make each sentence correct.

EXAMPLE: _2_ _2_ [1]Has/[2]Have Bob and Don [1]did/[2]done their work yet? (247, 204, 216)

_2_ _2_ 1 Yesterday I [1]give/[2]gave the monkeys several [1]handsful/[2]handfuls of peanuts. (193, 204, 216, 87)

_2_ _1_ 2 There [1]was/[2]were two squirrels [1]sitting/[2]setting on the wall. (239, 204, 217)

_1_ _1_ 3 [1]Doesn't/[2]Don't he know that the stolen car was [1]yours/[2]your's? (197, 146)

_2_ _1_ 4 Each of the men [1]were/[2]was in [1]his/[2]their place on time. (242, 163)

_2_ _1_ 5 Bob and I [1]seen/[2]saw several [1]deer/[2]deers last summer. (193, 204, 216, 89)

_1_ _2_ 6 [1]We/[2]Us sophomores could have [1]went/[2]gone with Joan and him. (151, 204, 216)

_1_ _1_ 7 King was [1]lying/[2]laying there while [1]we/[2]us three looked for him. (204, 217, 151)

_1_ _2_ 8 [1]Weren't/[2]Wasn't you here when we read about [1]Ed/[2]Ed's winning the car? (260, 127)

_2_ _1_ 9 Jo and [1]her/[2]she have [1]given/[2]gave it to me who am the leader. (149, 204, 216)

_1_ _2_ 10 Neither the boys nor Ann [1]is/[2]are to go with [1]we/[2]us girls. (238, 157)

_2_ _2_ 11 Both of her [1]sister-in-laws/[2]sisters-in-law receive high [1]salarys/[2]salaries. (86, 80)

_2_ _1_ 12 If I [1]was/[2]were you, I would [1]accept/[2]except the offer. (256, 228)

_1_ _1_ 13 Are you sure it was they [1]whom/[2]who we [1]saw/[2]seen today? (160, 204, 216)

_1_ _2_ 14 [1]Whomever/[2]Whoever we invite will please Jo and [1]she/[2]her. (162, 153)

_2_ _1_ 15 [1]Is/[2]Are Jan and her sister making all the [1]actors'/[2]actors costumes? (247, 121)

_1_ _2_ 16 I wish I [1]were/[2]was going to Paris with Jean and [1]she/[2]her. (256, 153)

_2_ _2_ 17 The [1]childrens'/[2]children's toys were [1]broke/[2]broken when we found them. (122, 185, 204)

_2_ _2_ 18 Bob and [1]him/[2]he should [1]of/[2]have shown it to us tutors. (149, 230)

_2_ _1_ 19 Either the twins or Dad [1]are/[2]is going to meet [1]us/[2]we travelers. (238, 157)

_1_ _1_ 20 He gave new [1]pianos/[2]pianoes to his [1]daughters-in-law/[2]daughter-in-laws. (78, 86)

VII. *Using Modifiers and Connectives in the Sentence* 20 Points

On the lines at the left, write the numbers of the bold-faced words that make each sentence correct.

EXAMPLE: _2_ _2_ I read [1]where/[2]that [1]those/[2]that kind of scissors is on sale now. (380, 302)

_1_ _2_ 1 [1]Almost/[2]Most all the participants played [1]like/[2]as if they were tired. (328, 372)

_2_ _1_ 2 Dan was [1]kind of/[2]rather frightened when he ran [1]into/[2]in the house. (333, 357)

<u>2</u> <u>2</u> 3 The six boys were angry ¹at/²with Al, for he didn't divide the money ¹between/²among them. (351, 354)

<u>2</u> <u>2</u> 4 It seems ¹like/²that he can't ¹never/²ever dive the right way. (372, 336)

<u>1</u> <u>1</u> 5 The players ¹surely/²sure do feel ¹bad/²badly about defaulting the game. (311, 312)

<u>2</u> <u>1</u> 6 Neither Ed ¹or/²nor Alicia sing well, but Ed sings the ¹better/²best. (378, 296)

<u>1</u> <u>2</u> 7 Sue finished her work ¹easily/²easy, but did not do it so ¹good/²well as Paul. (339, 329)

<u>1</u> <u>1</u> 8 His story ¹surely/²sure is different ¹from/²than the one that Ed told. (311, 337)

<u>1</u> <u>1</u> 9 We looked ¹behind/²in back of the sofa, but we didn't see ¹any/²no keys. (363, 336)

<u>2</u> <u>1</u>10 The ¹oldest/²older of the two brothers won't work unless you pay him ¹well/²good. (296, 329)

VIII. *Using Words in the Sentence*   40 Points

On the lines at the left write the numbers of the bold-faced words that make each sentence correct.

EXAMPLE: <u>2</u> <u>1</u> ¹Was/²Were you there when he ¹gave/²give the assignment? (260, 204, 216)

<u>1</u> <u>1</u> 1 I am sure that Liz will ¹teach/²learn Tom and ¹him/²he to swim. (227, 272)

<u>1</u> <u>1</u> 2 Jane ¹doesn't/²don't feel at all ¹bad/²badly about it. (197, 289, 312)

<u>2</u> <u>2</u> 3 That kind ¹of a/²of wide-brimmed hat looks ¹well/²good on Marie. (307, 289, 312)

<u>2</u> <u>2</u> 4 I read in the paper ¹where/²that they haven't found ¹no/²any clues. (380, 336)

<u>2</u> <u>1</u> 5 Sam may fail in math ¹except/²unless you and ¹I/²me help him. (370, 149)

<u>1</u> <u>1</u> 6 ¹Hull's/²Hull's and Smith's store has ten ¹basketfuls/²basketsful of plums. (124, 87)

<u>2</u> <u>2</u> 7 ¹Was/²Were Grace and Jean ¹setting/²sitting in Row C? (247, 204, 217)

<u>2</u> <u>1</u> 8 ¹Them/²Those campers won't listen to ¹us/²we leaders. (168, 157)

<u>1</u> <u>2</u> 9 Why can't she act ¹as/²like my two ¹sister-in-laws/²sisters-in-law do? (372, 86)

<u>2</u> <u>1</u>10 Neither Ruth ¹or/²nor Tina mentioned it to ¹us/²we reporters. (378, 157)

<u>2</u> <u>1</u>11 Every one of the men ¹were/²was in ¹his/²their own seat. (242, 163)

<u>2</u> <u>1</u>12 If I ¹was/²were she, I would ¹lie/²lay in the hammock. (256, 204, 217)

<u>1</u> <u>2</u>13 The ¹men's/²mens' ¹wifes/²wives are also doctors. (122, 82)

<u>2</u> <u>1</u>14 ¹Wasn't/²Weren't your books ¹lying/²laying on that table? (197, 204, 217)

<u>1</u> <u>1</u>15 He saw Mary and ¹me/²I when we ran from the car ¹into/²in the house. (153, 357)

<u>1</u> <u>2</u>16 Was it ¹she/²her whom you ¹seen/²saw? (152, 204, 216)

<u>2</u> <u>1</u>17 Each of the boys did ¹their/²his part very ¹well/²good indeed. (163, 329)

<u>1</u> <u>1</u>18 ¹Whomever/²Whoever you choose ¹should/²had ought to start working. (162, 225)

<u>2</u> <u>1</u>19 He is one of ¹them/²those persons who ¹are/²is naturally polite. (168, 241)

<u>2</u> <u>1</u>20 ¹These/²This kind of sheep ¹has/²have more wool. (302, 197)

SCORE _____ (Top Score 200)

Final Inventory/D

I. Sentence Sense

On the line before each group of words, write **o** if the group is not a complete sentence; write **1** if the group is one complete sentence; write **2** if the group is two sentences incorrectly written as one; or write **3** if the group is three sentences incorrectly written as one.

EXAMPLE: __o__ On the table where I laid it.

__1__ 1 The man over there on the corner is the one I asked.

__0__ 2 Wrote a letter to Laurie in Scotland today.

__1__ 3 Report to the director of physical training as soon as you finish.

__2__ 4 It was an excellent radio program, did you hear it?

__1__ 5 Wishing to see all the games, we bought season tickets.

__0__ 6 As I was driving along the highway in my new sports car.

__3__ 7 It will be a good game our team is sure to win you should be there.

__0__ 8 Writing stories for one of the leading magazines.

__1__ 9 Before we announce the class day plans, we must have the principal's approval.

__0__ 10 After the plans for the party have been completed.

Plain English Handbook, 1–4, 33–37.

II. Essential Parts of the Sentence   10 Points

On the first line before each sentence, write the simple subject. On the second line, write the simple predicate.

EXAMPLE:	*watch*	*Can be repaired*	Can this watch be easily repaired?
Mark	came		1 Down the street came Mark carrying a flag.
report	came		2 From the field came the loud report of a gun.
friend	Did remember		3 Did your friend remember to bring the pickles?
Neither	seemed		4 Neither of them seemed sad to be going.
row	was		5 There was a row of trees beside the road.

Plain English Handbook, 3, 4, 13, 15.

III. Classifying Sentences and Sentence Parts   30 Points

On the first line classify the sentence as to form by writing **S** for simple, **Cd** for compound, **Cx** for complex, or **Cd-Cx** for compound-complex. On the second line indicate whether the italicized group of words is a phrase or a clause by writing **P** or **C**. On the third line indicate the use of the phrase or clause by writing **n** for noun, **adj** for adjective, or **adv** for adverb.

EXAMPLE: __Cd-Cx__ __C__ __n__ The child accepted the money *that was offered him.*

__S__ __P__ __adj__ 1 That man *painting the picture* is a famous artist.

__Cx__ __C__ __adv__ 2 We saw Tom *as soon as he walked into the room.*

__Cx__ __C__ __adj__ 3 Is this the picture *that Dorothy painted?*

__S__ __P__ __n__ 4 Janet's ambition is *to become a doctor.*

__Cd-Cx__ __C__ __n__ 5 His ideas are good, but he wishes *that he could speak well.*

Cx	C	n	6 Lucile promised *that she would work for us.*
Cx	C	adv	7 *When the time comes,* Louisa will do her part.
Cx	C	adv	8 Don left *after the bell rang.*
Cd	P	adv	9 Both teams played well, but our team won *by a large score.*
Cd	P	adv	10 He tried his best, and he was praised *by all his friends.*

Plain English Handbook, 389–416.

IV. *Defective Sentences* 5 Points

Each item consists of two expressions of the same thought. On the line before each number write **A** or **B** to indicate which is the better sentence.

EXAMPLE: __A__ **A** Wandering through the shadowy woods, we enjoyed the day.
  B Wandering through the shadowy woods, the day was enjoyed.

__B__1 **A** To do one's duty is better than shirking one's responsibility.
  B To do one's duty is better than to shirk one's responsibility.

__B__2 **A** Jill is our class president, and she likes chess.
  B Jill, our class president, likes chess.

__A__3 **A** We drove nearly six hundred miles the second day.
  B We nearly drove six hundred miles the second day.

__B__4 **A** You gave an apple to the child that was green.
  B You gave the child an apple that was green.

__B__5 **A** Tom told George that he had been chosen captain.
  B Tom said, "George, you have been chosen captain."

Plain English Handbook, 433, 436, 439, 450–452.

V. *Capitalization and Punctuation in the Sentence* 45 Points

Indicate the changes needed in these sentences by writing the appropriate letter from the following key beside each number at the left.

a — capital letter	**d** — period	**g** — question mark	**j** — dash
b — small letter	**e** — semicolon	**h** — quotation marks	**k** — no change
c — comma	**f** — hyphen	**i** — colon	

EXAMPLE: 1 _d_ 2 _c_ 3 _d_ 4 _d_ 5 _a_   Dan's party will be on [1]friday[2] [3]april 15[4] [5]will you attend it? (469, 502, 486, 444, 464)

1 _k_ 2 _c_ 3 _k_ 4 _c_ 5 _c_ 1 In the [1]summer the flowers are pretty[2] [3]especially the roses[4] daisies[5] and petunias. (470, 499, 446, 504)

1 _k_ 2 _k_ 3 _d_ 4 _a_ 5 _g_ 2 I go to Wilson [1]High [2]School[3] [4]where do you attend school[5] (471, 445, 486, 464, 529)

1 _c_ 2 _h_ 3 _a_ 4 _h_ 5 _g_ 3 Who said[1] [2] [3]democracy must begin at home[4] [5] (501, 507, 466, 514)

1 _c_ 2 _d_ 3 _k_ 4 _a_ 5 _e_ 4 Bob[1] Mrs[2] Flint, the [3]principal of our school, comes from the [4]west[5] nevertheless, she is happy here. (500, 487, 481, 474, 490)

1 _c_ 2 _k_ 3 _a_ 4 _a_ 5 _c_ 5 Dick[1] when you visited your [2]aunt on [3]labor [4]day[5] did you meet Olga Williams? (500, 482, 469, 497)

1 _c_ 2 _k_ 3 _c_ 4 _c_ 5 _g_ 6 Did Miss Rand[1] your [2]English teacher[3] ever live in Dickens[4] Texas[5] (500, 471, 529)

1 _b_ 2 _i_ 3 _a_ 4 _b_ 5 _k_ 7 Many [1]Seniors are taking the following subjects[2] [3]spanish, [4]Sociology, and [5]history. (471, 493)

1 _f_ 2 _k_ 3 _a_ 4 _g_ 5 _h_ 8 "Did you know there were twenty [1] four people in our group when we visited [2]Carlsbad [3]caverns[4] [5] asked Fred. (534, 473, 484, 514, 507)

1 _a_ 2 _c_ 3 _j_ 4 _c_ 5 _c_ 9 The cover of our school magazine, [1]tiger Times[2] is decorated in our school colors[3] blue[4] white[5] and gold. (478, 500, 523, 504)

VI. *Using Substantives and Verbs in the Sentence*

On the lines at the left, write the numbers of the bold-faced words or phrases that make each sentence correct.

EXAMPLE: _1_ _1_ Those ¹knives/²knifes must have been ¹broken/²broke when we bought them. (82, 204)

_2_ _2_ 1 The pen was ¹laying/²lying there while ¹us/²we four were looking for it. (204, 217, 151)

_2_ _2_ 2 ¹Don't/²Doesn't Ricardo want to go with ¹we/²us hikers? (197, 157)

_1_ _1_ 3 There ¹were/²was three empty seats when Betty and I ¹came/²come in. (239, 204, 216)

_2_ _2_ 4 Here ¹comes/²come Joe and ¹him/²he with the popcorn for us. (247, 149)

_2_ _2_ 5 Is it ¹me/²I who am to direct the ¹boy's and girl's/²boys' and girls' games at an informal get-together? (152, 121)

_2_ _1_ 6 ¹Was/²Were the monkeys lying in their cage when you and Steve ¹saw/²seen them? (197, 204, 216)

_2_ _1_ 7 Paul and he were sure that the ¹ponys/²ponies were ¹ours/²our's. (80, 146)

_1_ _2_ 8 Fred and she ¹did/²done most of the ¹painters/²painters' work. (204, 416, 121)

_1_ _2_ 9 My mother ¹gave/²give Len and me four ¹cupsful/²cupfuls of sugar for fudge. (204, 416, 87)

_2_ _1_10 I am sure you ¹was/²were there when Julie told us about ¹Tom's/²Tom offering to sell tickets. (260, 127)

_2_ _1_11 I am sure it was ¹her/²she ¹whom/²who we saw at the poster exhibit. (152, 160)

_1_ _2_12 Either the scouts or their leader ¹is/²are responsible for repairing the ¹childrens'/²children's toys. (238, 122)

_1_ _1_13 ¹Have/²Has Connie and Ben ¹shown/²showed you the color photos of us? (247, 204)

_2_ _2_14 If I ¹was/²were she, I would ¹except/²accept the offer Roberto made. (256, 228)

_1_ _1_15 We will bring ¹whoever/²whomever will help you and ¹him/²he. (161, 153)

_1_ _2_16 Every one of the women ¹was/²were in ¹their/²her place ten minutes before the board meeting began. (246, 164)

_1_ _1_17 Neither Anna nor Jim ¹plans/²plan to do what ¹we/²us officers suggested. (238, 151)

_2_ _1_18 I wish Ann ¹was/²were going with ¹us/²we skiers. (256, 157)

_2_ _2_19 Both of his ¹son-in-laws/²sons-in-law sell and repair ¹radioes/²radios. (86, 79)

_2_ _1_20 ¹Us/²We photographers could ¹have/²of gone with Dick and him if we had only known it. (151, 230)

VII. *Using Modifiers and Connectives in the Sentence*

On the lines at the left, write the numbers of the bold-faced words that make each sentence correct.

EXAMPLE: _2_ _1_ The ¹most/²more bashful of the twins won't sing ¹unless/²without you urge him. (296, 370)

_1_ _2_ 1 This book ¹surely/²sure is different ¹than/²from the movie made from it. (311, 361)

_2_ _1_ 2 It seems ¹like/²that he won't do ¹anything/²nothing to help us. (372, 336)

<u>1</u> <u>2</u> 3 I looked ¹behind/²in back of the house, but there wasn't ¹no/²any cat. (363, 336)

<u>1</u> <u>1</u> 4 Kim and she ¹surely/²sure feel ¹bad/²badly about it. (311, 312)

<u>2</u> <u>1</u> 5 Will ¹these/²this kind of shoe wear very ¹well/²good? (302, 329)

<u>1</u> <u>2</u> 6 I read ¹that/²where the estate will be equally divided ¹between/²among the four heirs. (380, 354)

<u>1</u> <u>2</u> 7 ¹Almost/²Most all the singers acted as if they were angry ¹at/²with us. (328, 351)

<u>2</u> <u>1</u> 8 Neither Beth ¹or/²nor Mike can dance ¹very/²real well. (378, 311)

<u>1</u> <u>2</u> 9 Bob looked ¹rather/²kind of tired when he walked ¹in/²into the room. (333, 357)

<u>1</u> <u>1</u> 10 Neither Bill ¹nor/²or Janet skated very well, but I think Janet skated ¹better/²best. (378, 296)

VIII. *Using Words in the Sentence* 40 Points

On the lines at the left write the numbers of the bold-faced words that make each sentence correct.

EXAMPLE: <u>1</u> <u>1</u> ¹Are/²Is my hat and coat ¹lying/²laying on the bed? (247, 204, 217)

<u>2</u> <u>1</u> 1 Neither Bob ¹or/²nor Don ¹should/²had ought to carry the trunk. (378, 225)

<u>1</u> <u>2</u> 2 When we came ¹into/²in the house, we ¹seen/²saw Joan. (357, 204, 216)

<u>1</u> <u>2</u> 3 ¹Doesn't/²Don't each of the youths want to bring ¹their/²his father? (197, 163)

<u>2</u> <u>2</u> 4 ¹Us/²We girls were sure that the book was ¹your's/²yours. (151, 146)

<u>2</u> <u>1</u> 5 Why can't he ¹set/²sit down ¹as/²like he should? (204, 217, 372)

<u>2</u> <u>2</u> 6 ¹Them/²Those jars may fall ¹except/²unless you are careful. (168, 370)

<u>2</u> <u>2</u> 7 The ¹smallest/²smaller of the two brothers ¹weren't/²wasn't there. (296, 246)

<u>2</u> <u>2</u> 8 ¹Wasn't/²Weren't you here when the money was given to ¹we/²us treasurers? (260, 157)

<u>2</u> <u>2</u> 9 His ¹son-in-laws/²sons-in-law were ¹setting/²sitting on the porch. (86, 204, 217)

<u>1</u> <u>1</u> 10 The ¹workers'/²workers wet shoes were ¹lying/²laying on the floor. (121, 204, 217)

<u>2</u> <u>2</u> 11 If I ¹was/²were he, I would bring ¹whomever/²whoever would come. (256, 161)

<u>2</u> <u>2</u> 12 ¹Wasn't/²Weren't your parents in ¹Smith's/²Smith and Leon's store? (197, 124)

<u>2</u> <u>2</u> 13 Does this kind ¹of a/²of poncho look ¹well/²good on me? (307, 329)

<u>1</u> <u>2</u> 14 Jack feels ¹bad/²badly because he hasn't ¹no/²a ticket. (312, 336)

<u>2</u> <u>1</u> 15 Neither of the sopranos did ¹their/²her part very ¹well/²good. (163, 329)

<u>1</u> <u>1</u> 16 If I were ¹she/²her, I would ¹teach/²learn him to do it the right way. (152, 227)

<u>1</u> <u>1</u> 17 It's one of the stories that ¹are/²is different ¹from/²than the others. (241, 337)

<u>1</u> <u>2</u> 18 ¹Isn't/²Aren't ¹these/²this kind of tulip pretty? (197, 302)

<u>2</u> <u>2</u> 19 ¹Thiefs/²Thieves stole several ¹womens'/²women's watches. **(82, 122)**

<u>2</u> <u>1</u> 20 Did you read ¹where/²that Debbie and ¹she/²her had an accident? (380, 149)

128

SCORE _____ (Top Score 200)